Extra practice problems to help you succeed at

Math 20-1
Alberta

Problem
Solved

CASTLE ROCK
RESEARCH CORP

Rao, Gautam, 1961 –
    PROBLEM SOLVED: Mathematics 20-1
ISBN: 978-1-77044-340-2

    1. Mathematics– Juvenile Literature. I. Title

Publisher
Gautam Rao

Contributors
Jane Gannon
Victoria Garlitos
Pam Mosen

Published by
Castle Rock Research Corp.
2000 First & Jasper
10065 Jasper Avenue
Edmonton, AB T5J 3B1

    10 9 8 7 6 5 4

CASTLE ROCK
RESEARCH CORP

Dedicated to the memory of Dr. V. S. Rao

CONTENTS

RADICAL EXPRESSIONS AND EQUATIONS

SIMPLIFYING RADICAL EXPRESSIONS

Simplify each of the following radical expressions.

1. $\sqrt{90}$

2. $3\sqrt{16}$

3. $18\sqrt{2x^5}$

4. $7a\sqrt{68a^2b^2}$

5. $5\sqrt[3]{297}$

6. $2\sqrt{108x^8}$

Express the following mixed radicals as entire radicals.

7. $2\sqrt{7}$

8. $12x\sqrt{2}$

9. $3b^2\sqrt{13b}$

10. $\frac{1}{4}\sqrt[3]{320}$

11. Arrange the radicals $2\sqrt{13}$, $8\sqrt{2}$, $7\sqrt{8}$, $\sqrt{55}$, and $5\sqrt{4}$ in order from smallest to largest.

ADDING AND SUBTRACTING RADICALS

1. Simplify $2\sqrt{25} + \sqrt{25} - \sqrt{35} - 8$.

2. Simplify $-9\sqrt{32} + 2\sqrt{7} - 5\sqrt[3]{54} - \sqrt[3]{56}$.

3. When simplified, what does $\sqrt{99x^4} + 2\sqrt{11x^8}$ equal?

4. Given that $\sqrt{12} + \sqrt{27} - 5\sqrt{x} = 0$, solve for the variable x.

5. Evaluate $\sqrt{(16)(2)} - \sqrt{(9)(2)}$.

6. Add $y\sqrt{72x^5} + 2x\sqrt{18x^3y^2}$.

Use the following information to answer the next question.

A student has two lengths of string, measuring $\sqrt{25}$ and $\sqrt{16}$. A student's work to find the total length of string is shown.

$$\sqrt{25} + \sqrt{16}$$
$$= \sqrt{25+16}$$
$$= \sqrt{41}$$

7. Explain whether the student's work is correct.

MULTIPLYING AND DIVIDING RADICALS

1. Simplify $\left(2\sqrt{100}\right)\left(3\sqrt{100}\right)\left(\dfrac{1}{25}\sqrt{54}\right)$.

2. If $\left(a\sqrt{2}\right)\left(2\sqrt{5}\right)=8\sqrt{10}$, what is a?

3. Multiply $\left(3\sqrt{8x^2}\right)\left(4\sqrt{9x^5}\right)$, and simplify.

4. If the conjugate of $\left(2\sqrt{7}-3\sqrt{4}\right)$ is multiplied by $2\sqrt{7}$, what is the final result?

5. Simplify the expression $\dfrac{\sqrt{72}}{2\sqrt{5}}\times\dfrac{3\sqrt{54}}{2\sqrt{8}}$.

6. Evaluate $\dfrac{\sqrt{48}}{2\sqrt{3x}}$ for $x=2$.

7. Simplify the expression $\dfrac{2-\sqrt{3}}{\sqrt{5}+1}$.

SOLVING RADICAL EQUATIONS

Solve each of the following equations algebraically, and verify the solution values.

1. $\sqrt{x-2}=4$

2. $\sqrt{x^2+5}=5-x$

3. $\sqrt{x+2}=x$

4. $\sqrt{a^2+6}-a+3=0$

5. $2-\sqrt{2x-5}=x$

6. $\sqrt{4x+5}=2+\sqrt{2x-1}$

7. Write and solve a radical equation to find a positive real number that exceeds its square root by 6.

TOPIC PRACTICE QUESTIONS

1. Rewrite $3ab^2 \sqrt[3]{2}$ as an entire radical.

2. Rewrite $\sqrt{28x^3y^5}$ as a mixed radical.

3. Explain whether $\sqrt{25} - \sqrt{9}$ equals $\sqrt{16}$.

4. Write an equivalent form of the number 11 as an entire radical under a square root.

Simplify the following radical expressions.

5. $2\sqrt{98} + \sqrt{10} - 5\sqrt{8} - 3\sqrt{40}$

6. $\sqrt{125 + 71}$

7. $12\sqrt{2} \times 2\sqrt{3} \times 2\sqrt{2}$

8. $\sqrt{3}\left(2x^2\sqrt{6x} + \sqrt{6x^5}\right)$

9. $\dfrac{\sqrt{5}+1}{\sqrt{5}-1}$

10. $\dfrac{8\sqrt{18}}{24\sqrt{21}}$

Solve each of the following equations algebraically, and verify the solution values.

11. $\sqrt{1-x} = 3$

12. $\sqrt{a-3} = a-5$

13. $\sqrt{7y+2} - y = -4$

14. $\sqrt{12} + \sqrt{27} - 5\sqrt{m} = 0$

15. As an exact value, what is the measure of one side of a cube that has a volume of 200 cm^3?

16. Determine the value of x that satisfies the radical equation $\left(\sqrt{8x+20}\right)-\left(\sqrt{2x+5}\right)-3=0$.

RATIONAL EXPRESSIONS AND EQUATIONS

INTRODUCTION TO RATIONAL EXPRESSIONS AND NON-PERMISSIBLE VALUES

1. Which of the following expressions is a rational expression?

   A. $\dfrac{\sqrt{x}}{y}$

   B. $\sqrt{2}x$

   C. $\dfrac{24}{x^{\frac{3}{2}}}$

   D. $\sqrt[3]{x} + \sqrt[3]{8}$

2. Which of the following expressions is **not** a rational expression?

   A. $\dfrac{x-1}{x^2}$

   B. $x^{(2+2)}$

   C. $\dfrac{1}{x^{3x}}$

   D. $2x+7$

Determine the non-permissible values for the following rational expressions.

3. $\dfrac{(x+2)(2x)}{3(x-2)(x)}$

4. $\dfrac{5(x^2-1)}{x^2-9}$

5. $\dfrac{x+6}{6x^2-15x}$

6. $\dfrac{2+3x}{2(x+2)(x^2+5x+6)}$

SIMPLIFYING RATIONAL EXPRESSIONS

1. What are all the non-permissible values of x in the expression $\dfrac{(x+1)(x+2)}{(x+1)(x+3)}$?

    A. $x = 1$ and $x = 3$ **B.** $x = -1$ and $x = -3$

    C. $x = 1$, $x = 2$, and $x = 3$ **D.** $x = -1$, $x = -2$, and $x = -3$

2. Reduce the expression $\dfrac{3x^2 - 1}{x}$ if possible, stating any restrictions on the variable.

3. Write the expression $\dfrac{(x-2)}{(x^2 + x - 6)}$ in its simplest form, and state any non-permissible values of the variable.

4. Reduce the expression $\dfrac{x-1}{(x^2 - 1)}$, and compare the non-permissible values of the original and simplified forms.

5. Compare strategies for writing equivalent forms of rational expressions to the strategies for writing equivalent forms of rational numbers.

6. Reduce the expression $\dfrac{18-50y^2}{20y+12}$ to its simplest form, stating restrictions on the variable.

7. A particular volume of gas is defined by the polynomial $\left(x^3+2x^2\right)$ units^3. The gas is confined within a cube, which has a width of $(x+2)$ units. In simplest terms, write a rational expression that describes the ratio of the gas volume per unit of space. State the restrictions on the variable x.

Use the following information to answer the next question.

Marsha showed her work as she simplified the rational expression $\dfrac{a^2+12a}{2a}$:

$$\frac{a^2+12a}{2a}$$
$$=\frac{a(a+12)}{2a}$$
$$=\frac{a+12}{2}$$
$$=a+6$$

8. Identify and correct any errors that Marsha made in simplifying the rational expression.

MULTIPLYING RATIONAL EXPRESSIONS

1. Write the expression $\left(\dfrac{(x+1)^3}{24x}\right)\left(\dfrac{6(2x)}{2x^2-2}\right)$ in simplest form, and state any restrictions on the variable.

2. Simplify the expression $\left(\dfrac{3(x+1)^2}{4(x-1)^2}\right)\left(\dfrac{4(x+1)^2}{3(x-1)^2}\right)$, and state any NPVs.

3. Which of the following expressions is equivalent to $\dfrac{3}{x}$?

   A. $-\left(\dfrac{x}{3}\right)$

   B. $\left(\dfrac{2}{3}\right)\left(\dfrac{6}{x}\right)$

   C. $\left(\dfrac{3}{3x}\right)(2)$

   D. $\left(\dfrac{-x}{4x^2}\right)\left(\dfrac{-12x}{x}\right)$

4. Write the rational expression $\left(\dfrac{x^2-4}{x^2+5x-14}\right)\left(\dfrac{2x^2+14x}{2}\right)$ in simplest form, and list all NPVs.

Use the following information to answer the next question.

The rational expression $\dfrac{2}{x}$ is found as the result of multiplying two or more complex rational expressions (and reducing).

5. State two rational expressions that could give this result, and state any NPVs for these rational expressions.

6. State two rational expressions that could give this result, where $x \neq 4$ is a restriction on the variable.

7. Which of the following statements is **true** for the expression
$$\left(\frac{(x+1)(x+2)(x+3)...(x+n)}{1}\right)\left(\frac{1}{(x+1)(x+2)....(x+n-1)}\right)?$$

   A. After reducing, the numerator becomes $(x + n)$.

   B. After reducing, the denominator becomes zero.

   C. The expression cannot be simplified.

   D. There are n non-permissible values.

8. Simplify the rational expression $\dfrac{3x^3 + 2x^2 - 3x - 2}{x+1} \times \dfrac{15x}{9x^2 + 6x}$, and state any NPVs.

DIVIDING RATIONAL EXPRESSIONS

1. Simplify the expression $\dfrac{5}{\left(\dfrac{20}{x^2}\right)}$.

Use the following information to answer the next question.

A triangle has an area defined by the formula of base times height divided by 2. The base is represented by the expression $x^2 - 2x + 1$, and the height is represented by the expression $\left(\dfrac{2x}{x-1}\right)^2$.

2. Determine the area of the triangle in simplified form, and state any restrictions on the variable.

3. Which of the following expressions for y makes the equation $\dfrac{x}{3} \div y = \dfrac{2}{x}$ **true**?

   A. $y = \dfrac{x^2}{6}$ B. $y = \dfrac{6}{x}$

   C. $y = \dfrac{x}{2}$ D. $y = \dfrac{2x}{3x}$

4. Simplify and state the non-permissible values for the expression $\dfrac{x^2 - x - 12}{x+1} \div \dfrac{x^2 - 5x + 4}{x^2 - 1}$.

5. Reduce the expression $\dfrac{4(1-x)}{x} \div \dfrac{x-1}{2x}$, stating all NPVs.

6. Determine the value for b that will make the rational expression

$\dfrac{25-x^2}{bx} \div \dfrac{(5+x)}{2b} \div \dfrac{(x-5)}{-(bx-1)} \times \dfrac{x^2}{(bx-1)}$ simplify to $2x$. State all NPVs.

7. Which of the following statements about rational expressions is **false**?

   A. Simplifying eliminates NPVs.

   B. Restricted values are found only in denominators.

   C. If there are no variables, a fraction can still be undefined.

   D. Factors that are common to the numerator and denominator can be eliminated.

ADDING AND SUBTRACTING RATIONAL EXPRESSIONS

1. Perform the indicated operations, and simplify the expression $\dfrac{2}{3x} + \dfrac{3x}{4} - 1$.

2. When the rational expression $\dfrac{(x+1)(x-1)}{12x^2}$ has a new denominator of $12x^2(2x)$, it will have a new numerator of

   A. $2(x+1)(x-1)$ B. $6(x+1)(x-1)$

   C. $2x(x^2-1)$ D. $6x(x^2-1)$

3. Solve the expression $\dfrac{9y}{4} - \dfrac{x}{2} = \dfrac{y}{4}$ for x.

4. Simplify and state the NPVs for the expression $\dfrac{a+3}{(2a+2)} + \dfrac{a-1}{2(a+1)} - \dfrac{6}{a}$.

5. Simplify and state the non-permissible values for the expression $\dfrac{x^2 - 6x - 7}{x+1} - \dfrac{2x+12}{2x+2} + \dfrac{x+1}{x^2-1}$.

6. When the expression $\dfrac{2}{(1-x)} + \dfrac{x-1}{(x-1)(x)} - \dfrac{3}{(x-1)(x)}$ is simplified to a single rational expression, what value of x will produce a numerator of -3?

RATIONAL EQUATIONS AND PROBLEM SOLVING

1. Solve the rational equation $\dfrac{2}{x-1} = \dfrac{3}{x}$. State any restrictions on the variable.

2. Solve the equation $\dfrac{3x+1}{6x} = \dfrac{x+1}{2x+1}$, and state any NPVs.

3. Solve the equation $\dfrac{x}{x+1} = \dfrac{-2}{2x+2}$.

4. For the rational equation $\dfrac{2}{x} - \dfrac{5}{3x} = 4$, state the LCM and NPVs, and then solve.

5. What is the solution to $\dfrac{13}{y+1} = 4$?

    A. $y = \dfrac{3}{2}$ **B.** $y = \dfrac{9}{4}$

    C. $y = \dfrac{4}{9}$ **D.** $y = \dfrac{2}{3}$

Use the following information to answer the next question.

> One winter day, a child makes two perfect cubes out of snow. The child made each side of the second cube twice as long as each side of the first cube. The child's parent cuts each cube exactly in half and then puts one half from the small cube together with one half from the large cube. The parent determines that the total volume formed by adding one half of each cube is 36 cm³.

6. What is the side length of the small cube?

TOPIC PRACTICE QUESTIONS

1. Which of the following expressions is an equivalent form of $\dfrac{2}{(x-1)}$?

    A. $\dfrac{2x^2}{x^2-1}$

    B. $\dfrac{3}{6(x-1)}$

    C. $\dfrac{2(x^2-1)}{(x+1)}$

    D. $\dfrac{4}{2x-2}$

2. Simplify the expression $\dfrac{2x^2-x-1}{(6x+3)}$ by eliminating any common factors. State any non-permissible values for the variable.

Use the following information to answer the next question.

> A student would like to create a rational expression with two non-permissible values. The NPVs are $a=0$ and $a=1$.

3. Which of the following statements is **true**?

    A. The expression can have any number of factors involving the variable a in the numerator and denominator as long as after simplifying, the denominator only contains the factors of $(a)(a-1)$.

    B. The expression must have the variable x in the numerator and the factors $(a)(a-1)$ in the denominator.

    C. One possible expression that the student could use is $\dfrac{1}{(x)(x-1)}$.

    D. One possible expression that the student could use is $\dfrac{2}{2a^2-2a}$.

Use the following information to answer the next question.

> Rectangle A has an area that is represented by the expression $x^2 + 4x - 5$ and a width of $x - 1$.
> Rectangle B has an area represented by the expression $x^2 - 4$ and a width of $x - 2$.

4. Write an expression in simplified form for the length of rectangle A divided by the length of rectangle B. List any non-permissible values.

5. When the rational expression $\dfrac{(x+2)(x-3)}{(x-a)^2} \div \dfrac{x^2-x-6}{x-1}$ is simplified, the numerator is 1. Given this fact, solve for the unknown constant a. State all non-permissible values.

6. Simplify the expression $\dfrac{3}{x^2+2x} + \dfrac{x-1}{3x} - \dfrac{x^2+7x+10}{3x^2+15x}$, and state all NPVs.

7. Half of an unknown number is added to one quarter of the original unknown number, and the result is equal to 10. What is the unknown number?

8. Molly must obtain an average mark of 50% to pass her math course. There are six equally weighted tests in the course, and Molly received 50% on four of the tests and 52% on one of the tests. What is the minimum mark that she must achieve on her sixth test in order to pass the course?

TRIGONOMETRY

THE PRIMARY TRIGONOMETRIC RATIOS AND SPECIAL TRIANGLES

Use the following information to answer the next question.

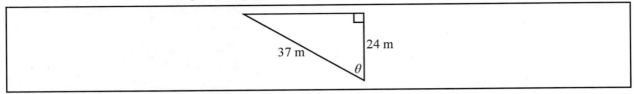

1. Find the measure of angle θ to the nearest tenth of a degree.

2. In a right triangle, $\tan\theta = \dfrac{12}{5}$. What is the exact value of $\cos\theta$?

Use the following information to answer the next question.

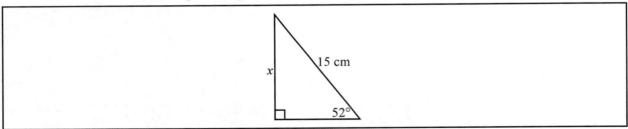

3. Find the length of side x to the nearest tenth of a centimetre.

4. Complete the following table by finding the exact value of each trigonometric ratio.

	$\sin\theta$	$\cos\theta$	$\tan\theta$
$\theta = 30°$			
$\theta = 45°$			
$\theta = 60°$			

ANGLES IN STANDARD POSITION

All angles are in standard position for the following questions.

1. Find the reference angle for a rotation angle of 205°.

2. Find the exact value of $\cos 240°$.

Use the following information to answer the next question.

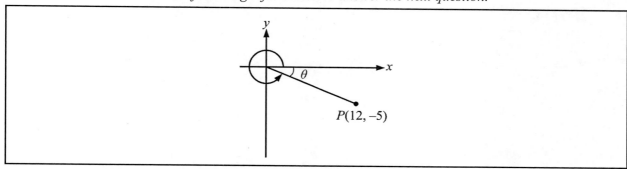

$P(12, -5)$

3. Find the exact values of $\sin\theta$, $\cos\theta$, and $\tan\theta$.

4. Which angle θ, where $0° \leq \theta < 360°,$ has the same cosine ratio as $210°$?

5. Solve $\sin \theta = 0.7071$ to the nearest degree, where $0° \leq \theta \leq 360°$.

6. Solve the equation $\tan \theta = 1$, where $0° \leq \theta < 360°$. Give exact value solutions.

THE SINE LAW

Use the following information to answer the next question.

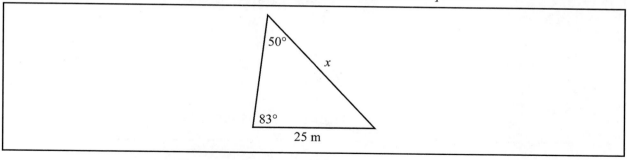

1. Find the length of side *x* rounded to the nearest tenth of a metre.

Use the following information to answer the next question.

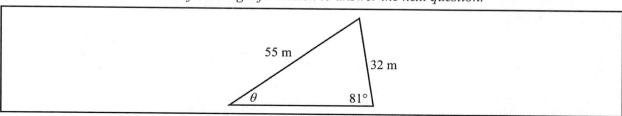

2. Find the measure of angle *θ* rounded to the nearest degree.

Use the following information to answer the next question.

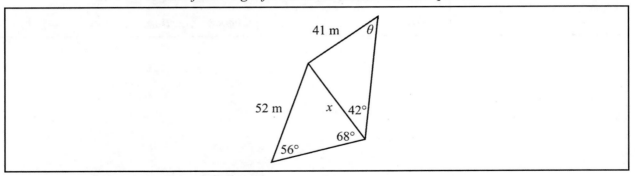

3. Find the length of side x and the measure of angle θ to the nearest metre and degree, respectively.

Use the following information to answer the next question.

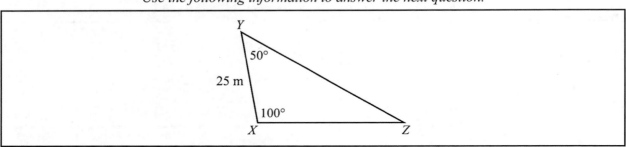

4. Determine the length of XZ to the nearest tenth of a metre.

THE COSINE LAW

For each of the following triangles, state whether the sine law or the cosine law should be used to determine the indicated side or angle.

1.

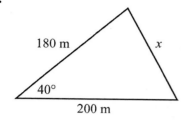

2.

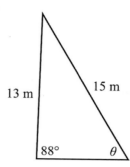

3.

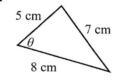

4.

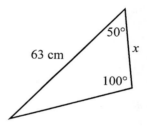

Use the following information to answer the next question.

A child is flying two kites at the same time. Both kites are 8.3 m above the ground, and the child is holding the kite strings 0.5 m off the ground. One kite string is at an angle of elevation of 35°, and the other is at an angle of elevation of 45°. The kites are 18 m apart.

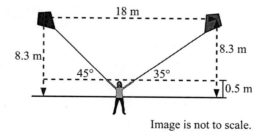

Image is not to scale.

5. What is the angle formed by the two kite strings to the nearest tenth?

TOPIC PRACTICE QUESTIONS

1. A right triangle has an acute angle θ. If $\sin\theta = \dfrac{7}{25}$, what is the exact value of $\cos\theta$?

2. Find the exact value of $\cos 315°$ in standard position.

3. If $P(0, 14)$ is on the terminal arm of angle θ in standard position, what are the exact values of $\sin\theta$, $\cos\theta$, and $\tan\theta$?

4. If $\angle\theta$ terminates in quadrant III and $\tan\theta = \dfrac{2}{7}$, what is the exact value of $\sin\theta$?

5. If $\cos\theta = -\dfrac{3}{5}$, where $0 \le \theta \le 360°$, then the value of θ to the nearest degree is

    A. 53°   **B.** 233°
    C. 53° and 127°   **D.** 127° and 233°

6. Solve the equation $\sin\theta = \cos\theta$, where $0° \le \theta < 360°$.

7. Solve $5\tan\theta - 1 = 3$, $0° \le \theta < 360°$, to the nearest tenth of a degree.

8. Which of the following formulas works only with right triangles?

A. $\dfrac{\sin A}{a} = \dfrac{\sin B}{b}$

B. $\tan A = \dfrac{\text{opposite}}{\text{adjacent}}$

C. $\cos A = \dfrac{b^2 + c^2 - a^2}{2bc}$

D. $a^2 = b^2 + c^2 - 2bc\cos A$

Use the following information to answer the next question.

A student would like to measure the height of a tower. From a point several metres from the base of the tower, she measures the angle of elevation to be 58°. She moves 10 m directly away from the tower. She takes another measurement and finds the angle of elevation to be 49°. The angle measurements were taken at her eye level, which is 1.45 m above the ground.

9. How high is the tower?

Use the following information to answer the next question.

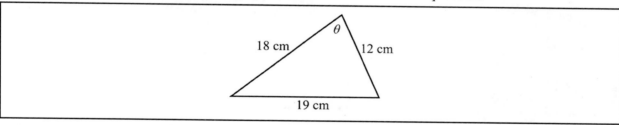

10. For the triangle shown, find θ to the nearest degree.

11. In $\triangle QRS$, $\angle R = 50°$, side $r = 10$ cm, and side $s = 12$ cm. Find the measures of $\angle Q$ to the nearest tenth of a degree.

FACTORING POLYNOMIALS

FACTORING USING DECOMPOSITION

Factor the following trinomials using the decomposition method.

1. $x^2 + 3x - 40$

2. $6x^2 - x - 15$

3. $9x^2 + 39x + 30$

4. $-10x^2 - 19x - 6$

FACTORING A PERFECT SQUARE TRINOMIAL AND A DIFFERENCE OF SQUARES

Factor the following polynomials.

1. $64x^2 - 144x + 81$

2. $4m^2 + 20m + 25$

3. $-4n^2 + 4n - 1$

4. $x^2 - 9y^2$

5. $9m^2 - 4n^2$

6. $-81 + 121y^2$

FACTORING POLYNOMIAL EXPRESSIONS WITH QUADRATIC PATTERNS

Factor the following trinomials using the decomposition method.

1. $(x^2+1)^2+(x^2+1)-6$

2. $2(x-9)^2-5(x-9)-3$

Factor the following difference of squares.

3. $4(x-7)^2-144(y+6)^2$

4. $16x^2-49(y-3)^2$

TOPIC PRACTICE QUESTIONS

Factor the following polynomials.

1. $x^2 - 4x - 21$

2. $2x^2 + 13x + 15$

3. $225x^2 - 30x + 1$

4. $24x^2 + 120x + 150$

5. $36x^2 - 49y^2$

6. $45x^2 - 125y^2$

7. $(x + 6)^2 - 8(x + 6) + 15$

8. $81(x - 7)^2 - 16y^2$

ABSOLUTE VALUE FUNCTIONS

THE ABSOLUTE VALUE OF REAL NUMBERS

Determine the value of each of the following expressions.

1. $|24 - 9|$

2. $|7 - 9|$

3. $|-7.2| + |16.3|$

4. $|-9| \times |6| \div |-3|$

5. $|-8 + 3| + |9| \times |-5|$

6. $|-4| - |12 - 2| \div |-5|$

7. $|-36 \div 2 - 10| \div |-7 \times -2| - |9|$

8. $|100 \div 5| \div |-4| + |-16 - 8| + |7|$

ANALYZING ABSOLUTE VALUE FUNCTIONS

Sketch each of the following absolute value functions. Rounding to the nearest tenth where necessary, state the intercepts and the domain and range.

1. $y = |x + 3|$

2. $y = |x - 7|$

3. $y = |-x - 4|$

4. $y = |x^2 - 6|$

5. $y = |x^2 + 6x - 5|$

6. $y = |-x^2 + 3x + 1|$

SOLVING ABSOLUTE VALUE EQUATIONS

Solve each of the following equations algebraically, and verify the solution values.

1. $-3 = -|3x - 1|$

2. $|3x - 4| = 2x + 1$

3. $|3x + 4| = 13$

4. $|x^2 + 6x + 5| = x + 1$

5. $|2x^2 + x - 6| = 4x + 3$

Use a graphing calculator to solve each of the following equations. Round solutions to the nearest tenth.

6. $|4x + 5| - x = 19$

7. $|x + 3| = |x - 1| + 6$

8. $|1 - 2x| = 12x - 7$

9. $|x| + |3 - x| = 12$

10. $|x^2 + x - 6| + |x| = 4$

TOPIC PRACTICE QUESTIONS

Evaluate each of the following expressions.

1. $\left|-6\right|+\left|9\right|\div\left|-2-1\right|$

2. $\left|6\div3\right|+\left|-4\right|-\left|-2\times5\right|$

3. $120+\left|9\div3\times2\right|-\left|-6-7\right|$

4. $\left|8\times(-3)\right|-\left|5-3\right|+\left|64\right|\div\left|-16\right|$

Sketch the following absolute value functions. State any intercepts and the domain and range, rounding to the nearest tenth where necessary.

5. $y=\left|-2x+9\right|$

6. $y=\left|3x^2-8\right|$

Solve each of the following equations algebraically, and verify the solution values.

7. $|4x - 3| = 77$

8. $|x^2 - 6| = 10$

Use a graphing calculator to solve each of the following equations. Round solutions to the nearest tenth.

9. $|9x - 2| + |x| = 12$

10. $|2x^2 - 15| = 4x$

QUADRATIC FUNCTIONS AND EQUATIONS

QUADRATIC FUNCTIONS IN THE FORM $y = a(x - p)^2 + q$

Identify whether the following are quadratic functions.

1. $y = \sqrt{x} + 5$

2. $p(x) = (x + 3)(x + 4)$

The following transformations have been applied to the graph of $y = x^2$. Write the equation of the graph of each transformed function in the form $y = a(x - p)^2 + q$.

3. A vertical stretch about the x-axis by a factor of 3

4. A translation of 9 units to the right and 8 units down

5. A reflection in the x-axis

The following equations represent a transformation or series of transformations applied to the graph of $y = x^2$. Describe the transformations that have occurred.

6. $y + 9 = (x + 9)^2$

7. $2y = -6(x - 5)^2 + 18$

8. Function f is the quadratic function defined by the equation $f(x) = \frac{1}{4}(x + 4)^2 - 11$. Function g is defined by the equation $g(x) = 4f(x - 1) + 2$. Determine the y-intercept of function g.

Use the following information to answer the next question.

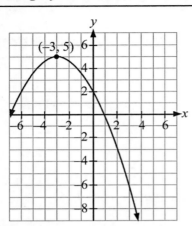

9. Identify the vertex, axis of symmetry, range, maximum or minimum, y-intercept, and x-intercepts.

Use the following information to answer the next question.

The following transformations are performed in the given order to the graph of the quadratic function $y = x^2$.

     i) A reflection in the x-axis

     ii) A vertical stretch about the x-axis by a factor of $\dfrac{2}{3}$

     iii) A horizontal translation of 2 units left

     iv) A vertical translation of 10 units up

10. If the point $(1, k)$ is on the graph of the transformed function, the value of k is _____.

11. The quadratic function $f(x) = x^2$ is transformed to the function $g(x) = \dfrac{1}{2}(x+3)^2 + 4$. The point $(2, 4)$ on the graph of function f is transformed to which point on the graph of function g?

  A. $(7, 4)$ **B.** $(7, 6)$

  C. $(-1, 4)$ **D.** $(-1, 6)$

12. Graph the functions $y = x^2 - 4$ and $-y = x^2 - 4$. Explain how the points on the graph of $y = x^2 - 4$ are transformed to the points on the graph of $-y = x^2 - 4$. Note the impact of the transformation on the intercepts.

QUADRATIC FUNCTIONS IN THE FORM $y = ax^2 + bx + c$

Convert each of the following equations to the form $y = ax^2 + bx + c$.

1. $y = 2(x+3)^2 + 5$

2. $3y = -\dfrac{3}{5}(x-5)^2 - 9$

Convert each of the following equations to the form $y = a(x-p)^2 + q$.

3. $y = x^2 - 12x - 5$

4. $y = -3x^2 + 12x - 1$

5. $y = \dfrac{1}{2}x^2 - 12x + 5$

6. $y = (x - 8)(x + 30)$

7. Find the vertex of the function $y = -3x^2 + 12x - 1$ using the vertex formula.

Use the following information to answer the next question.

Ronald completes the square for the equation $y = \dfrac{1}{4}x^2 - 80x + 11$. The steps of his solution are as follows:

1. $y = \dfrac{1}{4}\left(x^2 - 20x \quad\right) + 11$

2. $y = \dfrac{1}{4}\left(x^2 - 20x + 100 - 100\right) + 11$

3. $y = \dfrac{1}{4}\left(x^2 - 20x + 100\right) - 100 + 11$

4. $y = \dfrac{1}{4}(x - 10)^2 - 89$

8. Ronald's first mistake is made in step

    A. 1

    B. 2

    C. 3

    D. 4

APPLICATIONS OF QUADRATIC FUNCTIONS

1. If a farmer harvests his crop today, he will have 1 200 bushels worth $18 per bushel. For every week that he waits, the volume of his crop increases by 100 bushels, and the price per bushel drops by 50¢. When should the farmer harvest the crop to maximize his income, and what will be the maximum income amount?

2. A boat company has agreed to transport 75 students and charge $6.00 per student. The company agrees that for each student in excess of 75, the price per ticket for all students will decrease by 5¢.

   a) Assuming the boat has an unlimited capacity, how many students must be transported to generate the maximum possible income for the company?

   b) What should each student be charged in order to generate the maximum income?

   c) What is the maximum income that the boat company can generate?

3. A rectangular lot is to be fenced. One side is along a straight street where no fence is required. If 2 500 m of fencing material is available to build the other three sides, find the maximum area that can be enclosed and the dimensions that will produce this maximum area.

4. Separate 20 into two parts so that the sum of the squares of these two parts is a minimum.

5. A piece of string that is 40 cm long is cut into two parts so that the parts can be used as two perpendicular sides of a right triangle. Find the lengths of the sides that create the right triangle with the shortest possible hypotenuse.

6. A baseball is thrown vertically upward with an initial speed of 30 m/s. Its height, h, in metres above the ground at any time, t, in seconds is approximated by the function $h(t) = 30t - 5t^2$. Find when the baseball reaches its maximum height above ground and what the maximum height is.

SOLVING QUADRATIC EQUATIONS

Solve the following quadratic equations using factoring techniques.

1. $2x^2 + 5x - 12 = 0$

2. $\frac{2}{3}y^2 = 54$

3. Solve the quadratic equation $\left(y + \frac{2}{3}\right)^2 = \frac{25}{9}$ by taking the square root of both sides of the equation.

4. Solve the quadratic equation $b^2 = 7b + 11$ by completing the square.

5. Find the value of c so that $3x^2 - 2x + c = 0$ has two real and equal roots.

6. Write $0 = \frac{1}{2}(x-7)^2 + 5$ in the form of $-\frac{q}{a} = (x-p)^2$, and identify the number of solutions.

Solve the following equations using the quadratic formula.

7. $2y^2 + 11y = -15$

8. $\dfrac{2x-1}{3} = \dfrac{x^2+2x}{5}$

9. Find the exact values of the x-coordinates of the points where the graph of $y = 2x^2 + 4x + 2$ intersects the line $y = 6$.

10. Find the vertex, y-intercept, and x-intercepts as exact values for the graph of the function $y = (-3x - 2)(2x - 3)$.

11. Write the equation in the form $y = ax^2 + bx + c$ for a quadratic function that has zeros of -3 and 4 and passes through (5, 8).

APPLICATIONS OF QUADRATIC EQUATIONS

1. A baseball is hit such that its height in metres above the ground t seconds after it is hit is given by $h(t) = -5t^2 + 30t + 1$. Determine the exact times after being hit that the baseball reaches a height of 41 m.

2. Find two positive numbers with a difference of $2\sqrt{2}$ and a product of 2.

3. The sum of the length and width of a rectangle is 19 m. The area of the rectangle is 60 m². Determine the length and width of the rectangle.

TOPIC PRACTICE QUESTIONS

Use the following information to answer the next question.

The following transformations are applied in the given order to the graph of $y = x^2$:

- The graph is stretched about the x-axis by a factor of $\dfrac{1}{2}$.

- The graph is then reflected in the x-axis.
- The graph is finally translated 3 units right and 1 unit down.

1. Write the equation of the transformed function after each transformation.

2. In the correct order, describe the transformations that are applied to the graph of $y = x^2$ to give the graph of $3y = (x-5)^2 - 6$.

3. Use transformations to explain why the vertex of the function $y = (x - 0.5)^2 - 6.25$ is (0.5, –6.25). Use this vertex and any other information, such as the direction of opening, axis of symmetry, domain, range, and x- and y-intercepts, to sketch the graph of the transformed function.

4. A parabola has its vertex at (–2, –5) and its x-intercepts at $x = -3$ and $x = -1$. Write the equation for the parabola in the form $y = ax^2 + bx + c$.

5. For the equation of the function $y = x^2 + 8x + 18$, use an algebraic approach to find the vertex, equation of the axis of symmetry, domain, range, direction of opening, value of the maximum or minimum, and the x- and y-intercepts of its graph.

6. Find the values of a and c if the vertex of $y = ax^2 - 8x + c$ is (–4, 2).

7. Solve the equation $\dfrac{-3x^2 + 5}{2} = x - 1$ using the quadratic formula.

8. The zeros of a quadratic function are –3 and 8. The graph of the function passes through the point (1, 1). Write the equation of the function in the form $y = ax^2 + bx + c$.

9. Find the value of k so that $2x^2 - kx = -6$ has real and equal roots.

10. From experience, the organizers of a band concert know they can sell 6 000 tickets at \$20 each. From a survey, they determine that for every \$1 increase in ticket price, they will lose 200 customers.

    a) Write a function that relates the revenue from ticket sales to the number of increases in the price of each ticket.

b) Use the function to algebraically determine the ticket price that will bring the organizers the maximum revenue.

c) Determine the maximum revenue.

11. If one leg of a right triangle is 6 cm longer than the other leg and the hypotenuse is $5\sqrt{2}$ cm long, find the exact lengths of the two legs of the triangle.

12. A rock is thrown from the roof of a building. Its height in metres above the ground t seconds after it is thrown can be modelled by the equation $h(t) = -5t^2 + 10t + 15$. Give complete algebraic solutions to the following:

a) What is the height of the building?

b) For how many seconds is the rock in the air?

c) How long after the rock is thrown does it reach its maximum height?

d) What is the maximum height reached by the rock?

LINEAR AND QUADRATIC SYSTEMS

SOLVING A SYSTEM OF EQUATIONS GRAPHICALLY

Graphically solve each of the following systems of equations.

1. $y = 3x + 8$
    $y = x^2 + 4x - 12$

2. $y = 2x^2 - 10x + 10$
    $y = -3x^2 + 15x - 20$

Graphically solve each of the following systems of equations using technology. Give the solutions to the nearest hundredth.

3. $y = (3x - 5)(2x + 1)$
    $y = 2x^2 - 7x$

4. $y = x^2 - 2x + 3$
    $0 = 6x + y + 1$

5. $y + 9x = 3x^2 - 1$
    $y = -2x^2 + 7$

6. $y - 4x = -3$
    $8x^2 - 3 = -5x - y$

SOLVING A SYSTEM OF EQUATIONS ALGEBRAICALLY

Solve each of the following systems of equations by substitution.

1. ① $x^2 - 35x + 5 = y$
   ② $y = -4x - 25$

2. ① $y = 3 - 6x$
   ② $2x^2 + 8x = 3 - y$

3. ① $x = 5x^2 + y - 32$
   ② $-4x^2 - x = y + 3$

Solve each of the following systems of equations by elimination.

4. ① $-x^2 + y = 4x - 4$
   ② $-5x - y = -6$

5. ① $3y + 3x = 3x^2 + 15$
   ② $y + 4x = 3$

6. ① $\dfrac{1}{2}x^2 - 172 = y + 33x$
   ② $-\dfrac{3}{2}x^2 + 17x = y - 128$

7. Find two positive numbers, x and y, such that the difference between y and 12 times x is –69 and the difference between y and the square of x is –33.

CLASSIFYING SYSTEMS OF EQUATIONS

Using substitution or elimination, algebraically solve each of the following systems. Then, verify the solution graphically.

1. ① $4x - 4 = x^2 - y$
   ② $5 = 2x - y$

2. ① $y = x^2 + 3$
   ② $x^2 = 5 - y$

3. ① $y = (x-3)^2$
   ② $x^2 = y + 3$

Using substitution or elimination, algebraically solve each of the following systems.

4. ① $7x^2 + 9x + 6 = y$
   ② $3(3x+2) = y - 7x^2$

5. ① $y = -x + 4$
   ② $y + 1 = -(x-3)^2$

TOPIC PRACTICE QUESTIONS

Solve each of the following systems of equations algebraically, and verify the solutions using a graphing calculator.

1. ① $y = x^2 - 9x$
   ② $y + x = 9$

2. ① $y - x^2 = 15x - 160$
   ② $y - 33x = -2x^2 + 5$

3. ① $y = x^2 - x - 3$
   ② $2y = 10x + 26$

Solve each system of equations algebraically.

4. ① $6x^2 - 2y = -16x - 2$
   ② $8x - y = -3x^2 - 1$

5. ① $y = 25x + 47$
   ② $y + 3x^2 = x - 1$

6. ① $y - 17 = 3x^2 + 2x$
   ② $y + 2x^2 = 9$

Use the following information to answer the next question.

Bob and Kim each throw a ball into the air at the same time. Bob's throw is defined by the function $h(t) = -7.6(t-1.2)^2 + 15$, and Kim's throw is defined by the function $h(t) = -21.1(t-0.8)^2 + 15$, where $h(t)$ represents the height of the ball in metres at time, t, in seconds.

7. Rounded to the nearest hundredth of a second, at what times do the balls reach the same height?

Use the following information to answer the next question.

The distance, D, in metres that an accelerating car has travelled after starting from rest is given by $D = at^2 + b^2t$, where t represents the time in seconds.

8. If the car travelled 45 m after 1 s and 104 m after 2 s, what are the values of a and b if both are positive numbers?

LINEAR AND QUADRATIC INEQUALITIES

SOLVING QUADRATIC INEQUALITIES IN ONE VARIABLE GRAPHICALLY

Use a graph to solve each of the following quadratic inequalities, and show the solution on a number line.

1. $4x^2 < 2x$

2. $2x^2 + 5x \geq 12$

3. $6x^2 < 15x + 9$

Use a graphing calculator to solve each of the following inequalities. State the boundary values to the nearest tenth.

4. $2x^2 + 9x - 5 \leq 0$

5. $2x - 3 > -\dfrac{5}{2}x^2$

6. $-7x^2 \leq 3x - 8$

Use the following information to answer the next question.

During the summer months, Naya makes and sells necklaces on the beach. She projects that the profit, P, in dollars at the end of the summer season from selling a particular type of necklace can be modelled by the equation $P = -6x^2 + 240x - 350$, where x dollars is the selling price per necklace.

7. Find the selling price of the necklace so that Naya makes a profit of at least $1 450.

SOLVING QUADRATIC INEQUALITIES IN ONE VARIABLE WITHOUT A GRAPH

Use a number line and test points to solve each of the following inequalities. Graph solutions on a number line.

1. $3x^2 - 2x - 8 \leq 0$

2. $-x + 6 < 2x^2$

3. $x^2 + x - 12 > 18$

4. $x^2 \geq -11x - 24$

5. $-\dfrac{1}{3}x^2 - \dfrac{2}{3}x > -5$

6. Determine all pairs of integers that differ by 2 such that their product is less than 15.

LINEAR AND QUADRATIC INEQUALITIES
IN TWO VARIABLES

Using test points, graph the solution to each of the following inequalities.

1. $y \le -2x - 6$

2. $3x - 4y - 8 < 0$

3. $-\dfrac{y}{2} > x^2 - 2x$

4. $-y - 3 \ge -x^2 - 2x$

Use the following information to answer the next question.

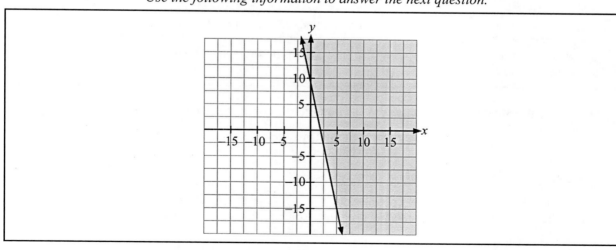

5. Determine the inequality that is displayed in the given graph.

Use the following information to answer the next question.

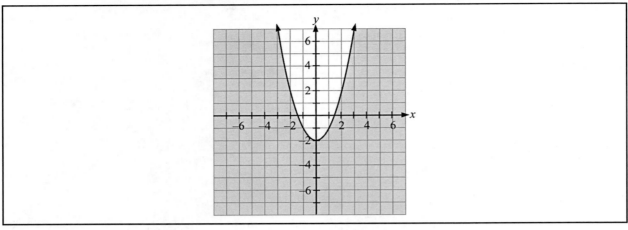

6. Determine the inequality that is displayed in the given graph.

Graph each of the following inequalities using a graphing calculator.

7. $\dfrac{9}{2}x - 8y \geq 6$

8. $\dfrac{5}{4}x^2 - 1 > -\dfrac{1}{4}y - \dfrac{11}{4}x$

Use the following information to answer the next two questions.

Fred and Andy decide to pool their money to buy a used motorcycle. The most that they will pay for a motorcycle is $500.

9. Determine the inequality that represents the amount of money that each will contribute.

10. Graph the inequality that represents the amount of money that each will contribute.

TOPIC PRACTICE QUESTIONS

Use the following information to answer the next question.

The graph of $f(x)$ is shown.

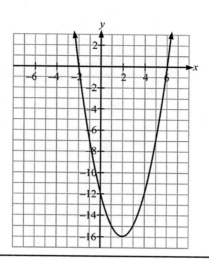

1. Determine the solution to the inequality $f(x) \leq 0$.

2. Use a number line and test points to solve the inequality $-x^2 \leq 5x - 36$. Show the solution on a number line.

3. Graph the inequality $\dfrac{3x - 52}{2} \geq 2y - 16$.

Use the following information to answer the next question.

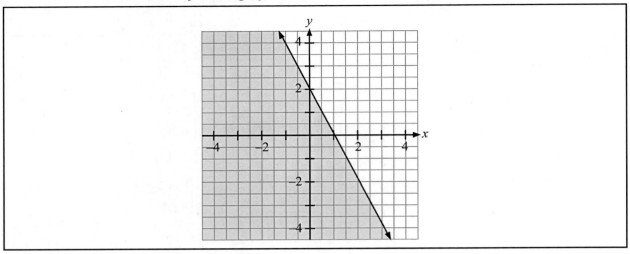

4. Determine the inequality that is displayed in the given graph.

5. Using test points, sketch the graph of the inequality $x^2 - 9x \le y + x$.

Use the following information to answer the next question.

From a bridge over a river, a stone is thrown upward. The height, h, of the stone above the river in metres is represented by the equation $h = 24.5 + 19.6t - 4.9t^2$, where t is the time in seconds after the stone was thrown.

6. Determine the times at which the rock is less than 39.2 m above the river.

Use the following information to answer the next two questions.

Lisa drinks two types of juice each day. Juice A is 15% lemon juice, and juice B is 40% lemon juice. Lisa can drink no more than 114 mL of lemon juice each day.

7. Determine the inequality that represents the amount of each juice that satisfies Lisa's requirements.

8. Graph the inequality that represents the amount of each juice that satisfies Lisa's requirements.

SEQUENCES AND SERIES

ARITHMETIC SEQUENCES

1. For the arithmetic sequence 15, –4, –23, …, generate the next five terms.

2. For the arithmetic sequence 3.5, 2, 0.5, …, find the general term and t_{30}.

3. If an arithmetic sequence is defined by the general term $t_n = 6n - 2$, find the first term and the common difference.

4. Insert five terms between 17 and –19 to form an arithmetic sequence.

5. If $(x + 6)$, $(7x)$, and $(9x + 2)$ are three successive terms of an arithmetic sequence, find x and write the numerical values of the first three terms of the sequence.

Use the following information to answer the next three questions.

Each summer, the price of an ice-cream cone increases by $0.15. In the 5th year, the cost of an ice-cream cone is $1.80.

6. How much did ice-cream cones cost in the 1st year?

7. How much will ice-cream cones cost in the 9th year?

8. When will ice-cream cones cost $3.45?

9. For the arithmetic sequence –4, 1, 6, 11, …, find the slope of the graph of the related linear function.

ARITHMETIC SERIES

1. Find S_8 for the arithmetic series $10 + \ldots -144$.

2. Find S_{11} for the arithmetic series $\dfrac{2}{5} + \dfrac{4}{5} + \dfrac{6}{5} \ldots$.

Use the following information to answer the next two questions.

The day after Halloween, Arnold counts 71 treats in his bag. He tells his mother that he will eat 2 treats on the first day, and each day after that, he will eat 3 more treats than the day before. His mother agrees only if he gives the rest of the treats to his brother and sister after 6 days.

3. How many treats will Arnold eat during the 6 days?

4. How many treats will Arnold give to his siblings after the 6th day?

5. The sum of the first 8 terms of a particular arithmetic series is 14, and the sum of the first 9 terms of the same series is 27. What is the 9th term of the series?

6. Find the sum of the arithmetic series $15 + 18 + 21 + \ldots + 45$.

7. Find the common difference of an arithmetic series if $S_{10} = -55$ and $t_1 = 8$.

GEOMETRIC SEQUENCES

1. For the geometric sequence $\sqrt{3}$, 3, $3\sqrt{3}$, ..., determine the value of r and find the next three terms in the sequence.

Use the following information to answer the next two questions.

David earns \$9.85 per hour. Each year, he gets a 6% increase in his wage.

2. What will his wage be in the third year?

3. In what year will he first be earning more than \$13.00 per hour?

4. Amorita's motorcycle is worth \$8 000, and it depreciates 16% each year. She plans to sell it when it is worth less than half of its current value. How long will she own it?

5. Find the first four terms of a geoemtric sequence if the general term formula is $t_n = 2(3)^{n-1}$.

6. If x, $x + 2$, and $x + 5$ are the first three terms of a geometric sequence, find the value of each term and the common ratio.

7. If the general term of a geometric sequence is $t_n = -6\,161(-0.235)^{n-1}$, find the value of the first term

8. Find the general term of the geometric sequence $-\dfrac{1}{8}, \dfrac{1}{10}, -\dfrac{2}{25}, \dfrac{8}{125}, \ldots$.

9. If $t_3 = 10\,000$ and $t_6 = 5\,120$ in a geometric sequence, find t_8.

GEOMETRIC SERIES

1. Find the sum of the geometric series $7 - 14 + 28 - 56 + \ldots - 3\ 584$.

2. If the general term of a geometric sequence is $t_n = -4(-3)^{n-1}$, find the sum of the first eight terms in the related geometric series.

3. Find the number of terms in a finite geometric series if the first term is -2, the common ratio is 5, and the sum of the series is $-7\ 812$.

4. Find the first term of a geometric series if the common ratio is 3.5 and the sum of the first four terms is $2\ 862$.

5. If $t_4 = 54$ and $t_6 = 24$ in a geometric series, find the value of S_{14} to the nearest tenth.

6. If $S_1 = 18$, $S_2 = 6$, and $S_3 = 14$, find the general term of the geometric series.

7. Find the sum of the geometric series $3\ 125 + 2\ 500 + 2\ 000 + \ldots$.

8. If the sum of the first n terms in a series is given by $S_n = n - 5n^2$, find the first three terms of the series and determine whether the series is geometric.

TOPIC PRACTICE QUESTIONS

Identify each of the following sequences as arithmetic, geometric, or neither.

1. $10, 9, 7, 4, 0, \ldots$

2. $-3, -12, -48, \ldots$

3. $2, 0.5, -1.0, \ldots$

4. $1, 11, 111, 1\,111, \ldots$

5. $\sqrt{7}, 7, 7\sqrt{7}, 49, \ldots$

6. $\dfrac{1}{3}, 1, \dfrac{5}{3}, \ldots$

7. Find t_n, t_{10}, and S_{10} for the arithmetic series $3.5 - 1.5 - 6.5 \ldots$

8. Find t_{15} in a particular arithmetic series where $S_{15} = 48$ and $S_{14} = 32$.

9. A math club starts with a certain number of members in week 1. Each week, 6 more people join. If there are 61 members in week 10, find the number of members in the first week.

Use the following information to answer the next two questions.

Theresa pulls 9 weeds from her garden one day, and each day after that she pulls 6 more weeds than the previous day.

10. How many weeds does she pull on the 7th day?

11. How many weeds has she pulled in total by the end of the 7th day?

12. If $t_4 = 46$ and $t_{12} = 102$ in an arithmetic sequence, find the number of terms that are less than 150.

13. If a car is initially worth \$32 000 and depreciates 17% each year, find its value at the end of three years.

14. Write the general term for the sequence $-3, 2, -\dfrac{4}{3}, \dfrac{8}{9}, \ldots$

15. If the general term of a geometric series is $t_n = -3(-2)^{n-1}$, find the sum of the first 10 terms.

16. Find the general term of the geometric series where $S_1 = 36$ and $S_2 = 24$.

17. Find the first two terms of a geometric sequence if $t_3 + t_4 = 50$ and $t_4 + t_5 = 100$.

18. A ball is dropped from a height of 12 m and bounces vertically to a height that is $\frac{2}{3}$ of the original height. On every successive bounce, the ball bounces to a height that is $\frac{2}{3}$ of the previous height. Find the total vertical distance, to the nearest tenth of a metre, that the ball has travelled when it hits the ground for the 8th time.

RECIPROCAL FUNCTIONS

ASYMPTOTES

Determine the asymptotes for the graphs of each of the following functions.

1. $y = \dfrac{1}{9x+6}$

2. $y = \dfrac{1}{10x-13}$

3. $y = -\dfrac{1}{6x+54}$

4. $y = \dfrac{1}{x^2+3x-4}$

5. $y = \dfrac{1}{121x^2-144}$

6. $y = \dfrac{1}{10x^2-14x+4}$

THE BEHAVIOUR OF THE GRAPH OF A RECIPROCAL FUNCTION

For each function, determine the invariant points and the behaviour of the graph as it approaches its asymptotes.

1. $y = \dfrac{1}{x+5}$

2. $y = \dfrac{1}{4x-28}$

3. $y = \dfrac{1}{2x^2-8}$

GRAPHING RECIPROCAL FUNCTIONS

1. Given $f(x) = 2x + 2$, sketch the graph of $y = \dfrac{1}{f(x)} = \dfrac{1}{2x+2}$.

Use the following information to answer the next question.

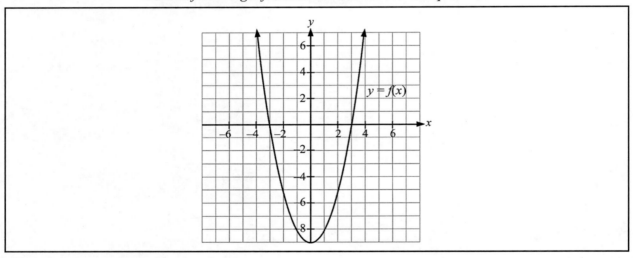

2. The graph of $y = f(x) = x^2 - 9$ is shown. Sketch the graph of $y = \dfrac{1}{f(x)}$.

TOPIC PRACTICE QUESTIONS

1. For $f(x) = 4x^2 - 4x - 48$, give all the asymptotes for $y = \dfrac{1}{f(x)}$.

2. What is the value of a, rounded to the nearest hundredth, in the function $y = \dfrac{1}{ax - 5}$ if there is a vertical asymptote at $x = 6$?

3. Given $f(x) = x + 3$, what are the points where the graphs of $y = f(x)$ and $y = \dfrac{1}{f(x)}$ intersect?

4. For the graphs of $f(x) = x^2 - 3x - 17$ and $y = \dfrac{1}{f(x)}$, where $y > 0$, the invariant points are

   A. $(-6, 1)$ and $(3, 1)$

   B. $(6, 1)$ and $(-3, 1)$

   C. $(9, 1)$ and $(-2, 1)$

   D. $(-9, 1)$ and $(2, 1)$

5. Determine the behaviour of the graph of $y = \dfrac{1}{3x - 48}$ as it approaches its asymptotes.

Use the following information to answer the next question.

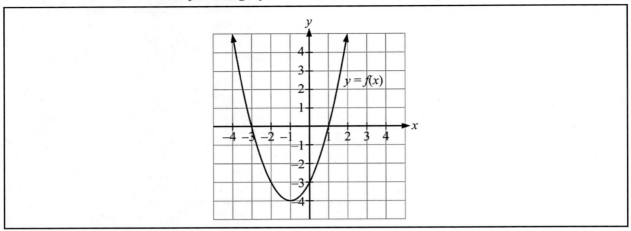

6. Given the graph of $y = f(x)$, what are the vertical asymptotes of $y = \dfrac{1}{f(x)}$?

7. Given $y = f(x) = x - 7$, sketch the graph of $y = \dfrac{1}{f(x)}$.

Answers and Solutions

Problem
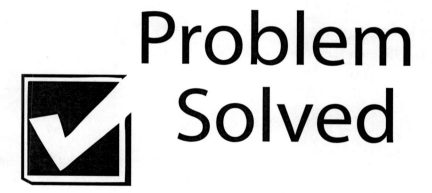 Solved

CASTLE ROCK
RESEARCH CORP

RADICAL EXPRESSIONS AND EQUATIONS

Simplifying Radical Expressions

ANSWERS AND SOLUTIONS

1. $\sqrt{90}$
$= \sqrt{9 \times 10}$
$= 3\sqrt{10}$

2. $3\sqrt{16}$
$= 3(4)$
$= 12$

3. $18\sqrt{2x^5}$
$= 18\sqrt{2(x^2)(x^2)(x)}$
$= 18(x)(x)\sqrt{2x}$
$= 18x^2\sqrt{2x}$

4. $7a\sqrt{68a^2b^2}$
$= 7a\sqrt{(4)(17)a^2b^2}$
$= 7a(2)(a)(b)\sqrt{17}$
$= 14a^2b\sqrt{17}$

5. $5\sqrt[3]{297}$
$= 5\sqrt[3]{27 \times 11}$
$= 15\sqrt[3]{11}$

6. $2\sqrt{108x^8}$
$= 2\sqrt{(36)(3)(x^2)(x^2)(x^2)(x^2)}$
$= 2(6)(x)(x)(x)(x)\sqrt{3}$
$= 12x^4\sqrt{3}$

7. $2\sqrt{7}$
$= \sqrt{2^2 \times 7}$
$= \sqrt{28}$

8. $12x\sqrt{2}$
$= \sqrt{(12^2)(x^2)(2)}$
$= \sqrt{288x^2}$

9. $3b^2\sqrt{13b}$
$= \sqrt{(3b^2)^2(13b)}$
$= \sqrt{(9b^4)(13b)}$
$= \sqrt{117b^5}$

10. $\frac{1}{4}\sqrt[3]{320}$
$= \sqrt[3]{\left(\frac{1}{4}\right)^3 \times 320}$
$= \sqrt[3]{5}$

11. Step 1
Find decimal approximations, or express the mixed radicals in entire form.

$2\sqrt{13}$ $8\sqrt{2}$ $7\sqrt{8}$
$= \sqrt{52}$ $= \sqrt{128}$ $= \sqrt{392}$
$\doteq 7.21$ $\doteq 11.31$ $\doteq 19.80$

$\sqrt{55}$ $5\sqrt{4}$
$\doteq 7.42$ $= \sqrt{100}$
                     $= 10$

Step 2
Compare the size of the radicands, and order them from smallest to largest.
$\sqrt{52}, \sqrt{55}, \sqrt{100}, \sqrt{128}, \sqrt{392}$

Step 3
Order the radicals in their original form from smallest to largest.

In order from smallest to largest, the radicals are $2\sqrt{13}, \sqrt{55}, 5\sqrt{4}, 8\sqrt{2}$, and $7\sqrt{8}$.

Adding and Subtracting Radicals

PRACTICE EXERCISES
ANSWERS AND SOLUTIONS

1. $2\sqrt{25} + \sqrt{25} - \sqrt{35} - 8$
$= 2(5) + 5 - \sqrt{35} - 8$
$= 7 - \sqrt{35}$

2. $-9\sqrt{32} + 2\sqrt{7} - 5\sqrt[3]{54} - \sqrt[3]{56}$
$= -9\sqrt{(16)(2)} + 2\sqrt{7} - 5\sqrt[3]{(27)(2)} - \sqrt[3]{(8)(7)}$
$= -36\sqrt{2} + 2\sqrt{7} - 15\sqrt[3]{2} - 2\sqrt[3]{7}$

3. $\sqrt{99x^4} + 2\sqrt{11x^8}$
$= \sqrt{(9)(11)(x^2)(x^2)} + 2\sqrt{11(x^2)(x^2)(x^2)(x^2)}$
$= 3x^2\sqrt{11} + 2x^4\sqrt{11}$

4. $\sqrt{12} + \sqrt{27} - 5\sqrt{x} = 0$
$2\sqrt{3} + 3\sqrt{3} - 5\sqrt{x} = 0$
$5\sqrt{3} - 5\sqrt{x} = 0$

For the equation to equal zero, $5\sqrt{3}$ will be subtracted from $5\sqrt{3}$.
$5\sqrt{3} - 5\sqrt{x} = 0$
$5\sqrt{3} - 5\sqrt{3} = 0$

Therefore, $x = 3$.

5. $\sqrt{(16)(2)} - \sqrt{(9)(2)}$
$= 4\sqrt{2} - 3\sqrt{2}$
$= \sqrt{2}$

6. $y\sqrt{72x^5} + 2x\sqrt{18x^3y^2}$
$= 6x^2y\sqrt{2x} + 6x^2y\sqrt{2x}$
$= 12x^2y\sqrt{2x}$

7. The student's work is not correct. To combine radicals, only the coefficients of like radicals are added.
$\sqrt{25} + \sqrt{16}$
$= 5 + 4$
$= 9$

Multiplying and Dividing Radicals

PRACTICE EXERCISES
ANSWERS AND SOLUTIONS

1. $\left(2\sqrt{100}\right)\left(3\sqrt{100}\right)\left(\dfrac{1}{25}\sqrt{54}\right)$
$= (20)(30)\left(\dfrac{3}{25}\sqrt{6}\right)$
$= 72\sqrt{6}$

2. **Step 1**
Simplify the left side of the equation.

$\left(a\sqrt{2}\right)\left(2\sqrt{5}\right) = 8\sqrt{10}$
$2a\sqrt{10} = 8\sqrt{10}$

Step 2
Solve for a.
$2a = 8$
$a = 4$

3. $\left(3\sqrt{8x^2}\right)\left(4\sqrt{9x^5}\right)$
$= 12\sqrt{72x^7}$
$= 12\left(\sqrt{36}\sqrt{2}\sqrt{x^2}\sqrt{x^2}\sqrt{x^2}\sqrt{x^1}\right)$
$= 72x^3\sqrt{2x}$

4. The conjugate of $\left(2\sqrt{7} - 3\sqrt{4}\right)$ is $\left(2\sqrt{7} + 3\sqrt{4}\right)$.
$2\sqrt{7}\left(2\sqrt{7} + 3\sqrt{4}\right)$
$= 2\sqrt{7}\left(2\sqrt{7}\right) + 2\sqrt{7}\left(3\sqrt{4}\right)$
$= 4(7) + 6\sqrt{28}$
$= 28 + 12\sqrt{7}$

5. $\dfrac{\sqrt{72}}{2\sqrt{5}} \times \dfrac{3\sqrt{54}}{2\sqrt{8}}$
$= \dfrac{6\sqrt{2}}{2\sqrt{5}} \times \dfrac{9\sqrt{6}}{4\sqrt{2}}$
$= \dfrac{54\sqrt{12}}{8\sqrt{10}}$
$= \dfrac{27\sqrt{6}}{4\sqrt{5}}\left(\dfrac{\sqrt{5}}{\sqrt{5}}\right)$
$= \dfrac{27\sqrt{30}}{20}$

6. Substitute $x = 2$, and simplify.
$\dfrac{\sqrt{48}}{2\sqrt{3x}}$
$= \dfrac{\sqrt{48}}{2\sqrt{3(2)}}$
$= \dfrac{4\sqrt{3}}{2\sqrt{6}}$
$= \dfrac{2}{\sqrt{2}}\left(\dfrac{\sqrt{2}}{\sqrt{2}}\right)$
$= \dfrac{2\sqrt{2}}{2}$
$= \sqrt{2}$

7. $\dfrac{2-\sqrt{3}}{\sqrt{5}+1}$

$= \dfrac{2-\sqrt{3}}{\sqrt{5}+1}\left(\dfrac{\sqrt{5}-1}{\sqrt{5}-1}\right)$

$= \dfrac{2\sqrt{5}-2-\sqrt{15}+\sqrt{3}}{5-\sqrt{5}+\sqrt{5}-1}$

$= \dfrac{2\sqrt{5}-2-\sqrt{15}+\sqrt{3}}{4}$

Solving Radical Equations

ANSWERS AND SOLUTIONS

1. **Step 1**
   Square both sides of the equation.
   $$\sqrt{x-2}=4$$
   $$\left(\sqrt{x-2}\right)^2=4^2$$
   $$x-2=16$$

   Step 2
   Solve for x.
   $$x-2=16$$
   $$x=18$$

   Step 3
   Verify the solution by substituting it into the original equation.

$x = 18$	
LHS	**RHS**
$\sqrt{18-2}$	4
$\sqrt{16}$	4
4	4

   Therefore, the solution is $x = 18$, or $\{18\}$.

2. **Step 1**
   Square both sides of the equation, and expand.
   $$\sqrt{x^2+5}=5-x$$
   $$\left(\sqrt{x^2+5}\right)^2=(5-x)^2$$
   $$x^2+5=(5-x)(5-x)$$
   $$x^2+5=25-10x+x^2$$

   Step 2
   Gather like terms, and solve for x.
   $$\cancel{x^2}+5=25-10x+\cancel{x^2}$$
   $$10x=20$$
   $$x=2$$

Step 3
Verify the solution by substituting it into the original equation.

$x = 2$	
LHS	**RHS**
$\sqrt{2^2+5}$	$5-2$
$\sqrt{9}$	3
3	3

Therefore, the solution is $x = 2$, or $\{2\}$.

3. **Step 1**
   Square both sides of the equation.
   $$\sqrt{x+2}=x$$
   $$\left(\sqrt{x+2}\right)^2=(x)^2$$
   $$x+2=x^2$$

   Step 2
   Write a quadratic equation equal to 0.
   $$x+2=x^2$$
   $$0=x^2-x-2$$

   Step 3
   Factor the quadratic equation, and solve for x.
   $$0=x^2-x-2$$
   $$0=(x+1)(x-2)$$
   $$x+1=0 \quad \text{or} \quad x-2=0$$
   $$x=-1 \qquad\qquad x=2$$

   Step 4
   Verify the solutions by substituting them into the original equation.

$x = -1$			$x = 2$	
LHS	**RHS**		**LHS**	**RHS**
$\sqrt{-1+2}$	-1		$\sqrt{2+2}$	2
$\sqrt{1}$	-1		$\sqrt{4}$	2
1	-1		2	2

   Therefore, the solution is $x = 2$, or $\{2\}$.

4. **Step 1**
   Isolate the radical on one side of the equation.
   $$\sqrt{a^2+6}-a+3=0$$
   $$\sqrt{a^2+6}=a-3$$

Step 2
Square both sides of the equation, and expand.
$$\sqrt{a^2+6}=a-3$$
$$\left(\sqrt{a^2+6}\right)^2=(a-3)^2$$
$$a^2+6=a^2-6a+9$$

Step 3
Gather like terms, and solve for x.
$$\cancel{a^2}+6=\cancel{a^2}-6a+9$$
$$6a=3$$
$$a=\frac{1}{2}$$

Step 4
Verify the solution by substituting it into the original equation.

$a=\dfrac{1}{2}$	
LHS	**RHS**
$\sqrt{\left(\frac{1}{2}\right)^2+6}-\frac{1}{2}+3$	0
$\sqrt{\frac{25}{4}}+\frac{5}{2}$	0
$\frac{5}{2}+\frac{5}{2}$	0
5	0

Therefore, there is no solution, or $\varnothing$.

5. **Step 1**
Isolate the radical on one side of the equation.
$$2-\sqrt{2x-5}=x$$
$$2-x=\sqrt{2x-5}$$

Step 2
Square both sides of the equation, and expand.
$$2-x=\sqrt{2x-5}$$
$$(2-x)^2=\left(\sqrt{2x-5}\right)^2$$
$$4-4x+x^2=2x-5$$

Step 3
Write a quadratic equation equal to 0.
$$4-4x+x^2=2x-5$$
$$x^2-6x+9=0$$

Step 4
Factor the quadratic equation, and solve for x.
$$x^2-6x+9=0$$
$$(x-3)(x-3)=0$$
$$x-3=0$$
$$x=3$$

Step 5
Verify the solution by substituting it into the original equation.

$x=3$	
LHS	**RHS**
$2-\sqrt{2(3)-5}$	3
$2-\sqrt{1}$	3
$2-1$	3
1	3

Therefore, there is no solution, or $\varnothing$.

6. **Step 1**
Since one of the radicals is already isolated, square both sides of the equation and expand.
$$\sqrt{4x+5}=2+\sqrt{2x-1}$$
$$\left(\sqrt{4x+5}\right)^2=\left(2+\sqrt{2x-1}\right)^2$$
$$4x+5=4+2\sqrt{2x-1}+2\sqrt{2x-1}+2x-1$$

Step 2
Gather like terms, and isolate the second radical on one side.
$$4x+5=4+2\sqrt{2x-1}+2\sqrt{2x-1}+2x-1$$
$$4x+5=3+2x+4\sqrt{2x-1}$$
$$2x+2=4\sqrt{2x-1}$$
$$x+1=2\sqrt{2x-1}$$

Step 3
Square both sides of the equation, and solve for x.
$$x+1=2\sqrt{2x-1}$$
$$(x+1)^2=\left(2\sqrt{2x-1}\right)^2$$
$$x^2+2x+1=4(2x-1)$$
$$x^2+2x+1=8x-4$$
$$x^2-6x+5=0$$

Step 4
Factor the quadratic equation, and solve for x.
$$x^2 - 6x + 5 = 0$$
$$(x-1)(x-5) = 0$$
$$x - 1 = 0 \quad \text{or} \quad x - 5 = 0$$
$$x = 1 \qquad\qquad x = 5$$

$x = 1$	
LHS	**RHS**
$\sqrt{4(1)+5}$	$2+\sqrt{2(1)-1}$
$\sqrt{9}$	$2+\sqrt{1}$
3	3

Step 5
Verify the solutions by substituting them into the original equation.

$x = 5$	
LHS	**RHS**
$\sqrt{4(5)+5}$	$2+\sqrt{2(5)-1}$
$\sqrt{25}$	$2+\sqrt{9}$
5	5

Therefore, the solutions are $x = 1$ and $x = 5$, or $\{1, 5\}$.

7. **Step 1**
Translate the word problem into an equation.
$$x = \sqrt{x} + 6$$

Step 2
Solve the radical equation.
$$x = \sqrt{x} + 6$$
$$(x-6)^2 = \left(\sqrt{x}\right)^2$$
$$x^2 - 12x + 36 = x$$
$$x^2 - 13x + 36 = 0$$
$$(x-4)(x-9) = 0$$
$$x - 4 = 0 \quad \text{or} \quad x - 9 = 0$$
$$x = 4 \qquad\qquad x = 9$$

Step 3
Verify the solutions by substituting them into the original equation.

$x = 4$	
LHS	**RHS**
4	$\sqrt{4}+6$
4	$2 + 6$
4	8

$x = 9$	
LHS	**RHS**
9	$\sqrt{9}+6$
9	$3 + 6$
9	9

Therefore, the solution is $x = 9$, or $\{9\}$.

Topic Practice Questions

ANSWERS AND SOLUTIONS

1. $3ab^2\sqrt[3]{2}$
$$= \sqrt[3]{\left(3ab^2\right)^3 (2)}$$
$$= \sqrt[3]{\left(27a^3b^6\right)(2)}$$
$$= \sqrt[3]{54a^3b^6}$$

2. $\sqrt{28x^3y^5}$
$$= \sqrt{4 \times 7 \times x^2 \times x \times y^2 \times y^2 \times y}$$
$$= 2xy^2\sqrt{7xy}$$

3. The equation $\sqrt{25} - \sqrt{9}$ does not equal $\sqrt{16}$.
   If each radical is simplified, the result is as follows:
$$\sqrt{25} - \sqrt{9} = \sqrt{16}$$
$$5 - 3 = 4$$
$$2 \neq 4$$

   The LHS does not equal the RHS of the equation, which means you cannot add or subtract radicals by combining the radicands. The correct way to combine radicals is to add or subtract the coefficients of like radicals:
$$a\sqrt{x} - b\sqrt{x} = (a-b)\sqrt{x}.$$

4. To write an equivalent form of the number 11 as an entire radical under a square root, use the concept of writing a mixed radical as an entire radical.
$$11 = \sqrt{11^2}$$
$$= \sqrt{121}$$

5. $2\sqrt{98} + \sqrt{10} - 5\sqrt{8} - 3\sqrt{40}$
$$= 2\sqrt{49}\sqrt{2} + \sqrt{10} - 5\sqrt{4}\sqrt{2} - 3\sqrt{4}\sqrt{10}$$
$$= 14\sqrt{2} + \sqrt{10} - 10\sqrt{2} - 6\sqrt{10}$$
$$= 4\sqrt{2} - 5\sqrt{10}$$

6. $\sqrt{125+71}$
   $=\sqrt{196}$
   $=14$

7. $12\sqrt{2}\times2\sqrt{3}\times2\sqrt{2}$
   $=48\sqrt{12}$
   $=48\sqrt{4}\sqrt{3}$
   $=96\sqrt{3}$

8. $\sqrt{3}\left(2x^2\sqrt{6x}+\sqrt{6x^5}\right)$
   $=\sqrt{3}\left(2x^2\sqrt{6x}\right)+\sqrt{3}\left(\sqrt{6x^5}\right)$
   $=2x^2\sqrt{18x}+\sqrt{18x^5}$
   $=2x^2\sqrt{9}\sqrt{2x}+\sqrt{9x^4}\sqrt{2x}$
   $=6x^2\sqrt{2x}+3x^2\sqrt{2x}$
   $=9x^2\sqrt{2x}$

   As an alternate solution, you could simplify the terms in the brackets first.
   $\sqrt{3}\left(2x^2\sqrt{6x}+\sqrt{6x^5}\right)$
   $=\sqrt{3}\left(2x^2\sqrt{6x}+x^2\sqrt{6x}\right)$
   $=\sqrt{3}\left(3x^2\sqrt{6x}\right)$
   $=3x^2\sqrt{18x}$
   $=9x^2\sqrt{2x}$

9. $\dfrac{\sqrt{5}+1}{\sqrt{5}-1}$
   $=\left(\dfrac{\sqrt{5}+1}{\sqrt{5}-1}\right)\left(\dfrac{\sqrt{5}+1}{\sqrt{5}+1}\right)$
   $=\dfrac{5+\sqrt{5}+\sqrt{5}+1}{5+\sqrt{5}-\sqrt{5}-1}$
   $=\dfrac{6+2\sqrt{5}}{4}$
   $=\dfrac{3+\sqrt{5}}{2}$

10. $\dfrac{8\sqrt{18}}{24\sqrt{21}}$
    $=\dfrac{\sqrt{6}}{3\sqrt{7}}$
    $=\dfrac{\sqrt{6}}{3\sqrt{7}}\left(\dfrac{\sqrt{7}}{\sqrt{7}}\right)$
    $=\dfrac{\sqrt{42}}{21}$

11. **Step 1**
    Square both sides of the equation.
    $\sqrt{1-x}=3$
    $\left(\sqrt{1-x}\right)^2=(3)^2$
    $1-x=9$

    Step 2
    Solve for x.
    $1-x=9$
    $-8=x$

    Step 3
    Verify the solution by substituting it into the original equation.

$x=-8$	
LHS	RHS
$\sqrt{1-(-8)}$	3
$\sqrt{9}$	3
3	3

    Therefore, the solution is $x=-8$, or $\{-8\}$.

12. **Step 1**
    Square both sides of the equation, and expand.
    $\sqrt{a-3}=a-5$
    $\left(\sqrt{a-3}\right)^2=(a-5)^2$
    $a-3=a^2-10a+25$

    Step 2
    Write a quadratic equation equal to 0.
    $a-3=a^2-10a+25$
    $0=a^2-11a+28$

    Step 3
    Factor the quadratic equation, and solve for x.
    $0=a^2-11a+28$
    $0=(a-4)(a-7)$
    $a-4=0$ or $a-7=0$
    $a=4$ $\quad$ $a=7$

    Step 4
    Verify the solutions by substituting them into the original equation.

$a=4$		$a=7$	
LHS	RHS	LHS	RHS
$\sqrt{4-3}$	$4-5$	$\sqrt{7-3}$	$7-5$
$\sqrt{1}$	-1	$\sqrt{4}$	2
1	-1	2	2

Therefore, the solution is $a = 7$, or $\{7\}$.

13. Step 1
Isolate the radical on one side of the equation.
$$\sqrt{7y+2} - y = -4$$
$$\sqrt{7y+2} = -4 + y$$

Step 2
Square both sides of the equation, and expand.
$$\left(\sqrt{7y+2}\right)^2 = (-4+y)^2$$
$$7y+2 = 16 - 8y + y^2$$

Step 3
Gather like terms, and solve for y.
$$7y+2 = 16 - 8y + y^2$$
$$0 = y^2 - 15y + 14$$
$$0 = (y-1)(y-14)$$
$$y-1=0 \quad \text{or} \quad y-14=0$$
$$y=1 \qquad\qquad y=14$$

Step 4
Verify the solutions by substituting them into the original equation.

$y = 1$			$y = 14$	
LHS	**RHS**		**LHS**	**RHS**
$\sqrt{7(1)+2}-(1)$	-4		$\sqrt{7(14)+2}-(14)$	-4
$\sqrt{9}-1$	-4		$\sqrt{100}-14$	-4
2	-4		$10-14$	-4
			-4	-4

Therefore, the solution is $y = 14$, or $\{14\}$.

14. Step 1
Isolate the radical with the variable on one side of the equation.
$$\sqrt{12} + \sqrt{27} - 5\sqrt{m} = 0$$
$$\sqrt{12} + \sqrt{27} = 5\sqrt{m}$$

Step 2
Simplify the left side of the equation.
$$\sqrt{12} + \sqrt{27} = 5\sqrt{m}$$
$$2\sqrt{3} + 3\sqrt{3} = 5\sqrt{m}$$
$$5\sqrt{3} = 5\sqrt{m}$$

Step 3
Solve for m. Since $5\sqrt{3} = 5\sqrt{m}$, then $m = 3$.

15. The formula for the volume of a cube is $V = s^3$, where V is the volume and s is the side length. Substitute the volume measure into the formula, and solve for s.
$$V = s^3$$
$$200 = s^3$$
$$\sqrt[3]{200} = s$$
$$\sqrt[3]{8} \times \sqrt[3]{25} = s$$
$$2\sqrt[3]{25} = s$$

The measure of one side of a cube with a volume of 200 cm^3 is $2\sqrt[3]{25}$ cm.

16. Step 1
Isolate the more complex radical.
$$\left(\sqrt{8x+20}\right) - \left(\sqrt{2x+5}\right) - 3 = 0$$
$$\left(\sqrt{8x+20}\right) = \sqrt{2x+5} + 3$$

Step 2
Square both sides of the equation, and expand.
$$\left(\sqrt{8x+20}\right) = \sqrt{2x+5} + 3$$
$$\left(\sqrt{8x+20}\right)^2 = \left(\sqrt{2x+5}+3\right)^2$$
$$8x+20 = \left(\sqrt{2x+5}+3\right)\left(\sqrt{2x+5}+3\right)$$
$$8x+20 = (2x+5) + 6\sqrt{2x+5} + 9$$

Step 3
Collect like terms, and isolate the radical on one side.
$$8x+20 = (2x+5) + 6\sqrt{2x+5} + 9$$
$$8x+20 = 2x+14 + 6\sqrt{2x+5}$$
$$6x+6 = 6\sqrt{2x+5}$$
$$x+1 = \sqrt{2x+5}$$

Step 4
Square both sides of the equation, and set up a quadratic equation.
$$x+1 = \sqrt{2x+5}$$
$$(x+1)^2 = \left(\sqrt{2x+5}\right)^2$$
$$x^2 + 2x + 1 = 2x + 5$$
$$x^2 - 4 = 0$$

Step 5
Factor the difference of squares, and solve for x.
$$x^2 - 4 = 0$$
$$(x+2)(x-2) = 0$$
$$x + 2 = 0 \quad \text{or} \quad x - 2 = 0$$
$$x = -2 \qquad\qquad x = 2$$

Step 6
Verify the solutions by substituting them into the original equation.

$x = -2$	
LHS	**RHS**
$\left(\sqrt{8(-2)+20}\right) - \left(\sqrt{2(-2)+5}\right) - 3$	0
$\left(\sqrt{4}\right) - \left(\sqrt{1}\right) - 3$	0
-2	0

$x = 2$	
LHS	**RHS**
$\left(\sqrt{8(2)+20}\right) - \left(\sqrt{2(2)+5}\right) - 3$	0
$\left(\sqrt{36}\right) - \left(\sqrt{9}\right) - 3$	0
0	0

Therefore, the solution is $x = 2$, or $\{2\}$.

RATIONAL EXPRESSIONS AND EQUATIONS

Introduction to Rational Expressions and Non-Permissible Values

ANSWERS AND SOLUTIONS

1. **B**

The expression $\sqrt{2}x$ is rational because the radical sign ($\sqrt{\ }$) does not include the variable, and the expression could be written as a fraction, $\frac{\sqrt{2}x}{1}$.

The expressions $\frac{\sqrt{x}}{y}$, $\frac{24}{x^{\frac{3}{2}}}$, and $\sqrt[3]{x} + \sqrt[3]{8}$ each contain terms where the variables have fractional degrees.

2. **C**

The expression $\frac{1}{x^{3x}}$ is not rational because there is a variable exponent in the denominator. Therefore, the denominator is not a polynomial.

The expression $x^{(2+2)}$ has an unusual notation for the exponent, but the exponent is still an integer, making it rational. The expressions $\frac{x-1}{x^2}$ and $2x + 7$ are quotients of two polynomials, where the latter has a denominator of 1.

3. If $(x-2)$ or (x) in the denominator equals 0, the expression $\frac{(x+2)(2x)}{3(x-2)(x)}$ is undefined.
Therefore, $x \neq 0$ and $x \neq 2$.

4. If $\left(x^2 - 9\right)$ in the denominator equals 0, the expression $\frac{5\left(x^2 - 1\right)}{x^2 - 9}$ is undefined.
$$x^2 - 9 = 0$$
$$(x-3)(x+3) = 0$$
$$x - 3 = 0 \quad \text{or} \quad x + 3 = 0$$
$$x = 3 \qquad\qquad x = -3$$
Therefore, $x \neq 3$ and $x \neq -3$.

5. If $(6x^2 - 15x)$ in the denominator equals 0, the

expression $\dfrac{x+6}{6x^2-15x}$ is undefined.

$$6x^2 - 15x = 0$$
$$3x(2x-5) = 0$$

Therefore, $x \neq 0$ and $x \neq \dfrac{5}{2}$.

6. If $(x + 2)$ or $(x^2 + 5x + 6)$ in the denominator

equals 0, the expression $\dfrac{2+3x}{2(x+2)(x^2+5x+6)}$

is undefined.

$$x + 2 = 0 \quad \text{or} \quad x^2 + 5x + 6 = 0$$
$$x = -2 \qquad\qquad (x+2)(x+3) = 0$$
$$x = -2, -3$$

Therefore, $x \neq -2$ and $x \neq -3$. It is not necessary to list the -2 value twice.

Simplifying Rational Expressions

ANSWERS AND SOLUTIONS

1. B

If $(x + 1)$ or $(x + 3)$ in the denominator equals 0,

the expression $\dfrac{(x+1)(x+2)}{(x+1)(x+3)}$ is undefined.

Therefore, the NPVs are $x = -1$ and $x = -3$.

2. There are no common factors to eliminate, so the

expression $\dfrac{3x^2-1}{x}$ is in its simplest form already,

where $x \neq 0$.

3. Factor where possible, and eliminate common factors to simplify the expression.

The NPVs can be identified using the original denominator in factored form.

$$\frac{(x-2)}{(x^2+x-6)}$$
$$= \frac{\cancel{x-2}}{(\cancel{x-2})(x+3)}$$
$$= \frac{1}{x+3}, x \neq 2, -3$$

4. Factor where possible, and eliminate common factors to simplify the expression.

The NPVs can be identified using the original denominator in factored form.

$$\frac{x-1}{(x^2-1)}$$
$$= \frac{\cancel{x-1}}{(\cancel{x-1})(x+1)}$$
$$= \frac{1}{x+1}, x \neq \pm 1$$

Comparing the NPVs of the original and simplified forms, you can see that the NPVs of the original denominator are 1 and -1, but the NPV of the simplified form is just -1. However, both 1 and -1 must be stated as restrictions in the solution for the expressions to be equivalent. The original and simplified forms are equivalent only when all the NPVs are identified.

5. The strategies are the same for writing equivalent forms of rational numbers and expressions.

One method is to multiply the numerator and denominator by the same value.

Rational numbers:

$$\frac{2}{7}\left(\frac{3}{3}\right) = \frac{6}{21}$$

Rational expressions:

$$\frac{x^2}{2+x}\left(\frac{3x}{3x}\right) = \frac{3x^3}{6x+3x^2}, x \neq -2, 0$$

In these examples, $\dfrac{2}{7}$ is equivalent to $\dfrac{6}{21}$,

and $\dfrac{x^2}{2+x}$ is equivalent to $\dfrac{3x^3}{6x+3x^2}$.

Another method is to simplify the numerator and denominator by dividing (reducing) by a common factor.

Rational numbers:

$$\frac{8}{36} = \frac{(\cancel{4})(2)}{(\cancel{4})(9)}$$
$$= \frac{2}{9}$$

Rational expressions:

$$\frac{12x-3}{3x^2}$$

$$=\frac{\cancel{3}(4x-1)}{\cancel{3}x^2}$$

$$=\frac{4x-1}{x^2}, x \neq 0$$

In these examples, $\frac{8}{36}$ is equivalent to $\frac{2}{9}$,

and $\frac{12x-3}{3x^2}$ is equivalent to $\frac{4x-1}{x^2}$.

The NPVs must be stated for rational expressions.

6. Factor where possible, and eliminate common factors to simplify the expression.

The NPVs can be identified using the original denominator in factored form.

$$\frac{18-50y^2}{20y+12}$$

$$=\frac{2(9-25y^2)}{4(5y+3)}$$

$$=\frac{\cancel{2}(3-5y)\cancel{(3+5y)}}{\cancel{4}(5y+3)}$$

$$=\frac{3-5y}{2}, y \neq -\frac{3}{5}$$

In this question, it is important to recognize that the numerator contains a difference of squares, and that the factors $(3+5y)$ and $(5y+3)$ are the same.

7. Write a ratio comparing gas volume per unit of space.

The gas volume (x^3+2x^2) will be in the numerator, and the cubic space $(x+2)^3$ will be in the denominator. The $(x+2)$ in the denominator is cubed since the length and height are the same as the width in a cube. The units will cancel each other since both the numerator and denominator are now in units^3.

$$\frac{x^3+2x^2}{(x+2)^3}$$

$$=\frac{x^2\cancel{(x+2)}}{(x+2)(x+2)\cancel{(x+2)}}$$

$$=\frac{x^2}{(x+2)^2}$$

This is the most reduced form as a rational expression. It could also be written as the ratio $x^2 : (x+2)^2$.

The NPVs can be identified using the original denominator in factored form. Therefore, $x \neq -2$.

Note that this is the complete answer, but the value of $(x+2)$ units is given as the width of an actual cubic space. As such, if x were less than -2, there would have been a negative dimension to the object, and this would not exist in real space.

8. Simplify the expression by factoring where possible.

$$\frac{a^2+12a}{2a} = \frac{a(a+12)}{2a}$$

Eliminate the common factors, and state any NPVs.

$$\frac{\cancel{a}(a+12)}{2\cancel{a}} = \frac{a+12}{2}, a \neq 0$$

This is in simplest form since there are no more common factors in the numerator and denominator. You cannot reduce the 12 and 2 because 2 is not a factor common to both terms in the numerator. Therefore, the final step is not correct in Marsha's solution.

The correct solution is as follows:

$$\frac{a^2+12a}{2a}$$

$$=\frac{a(a+12)}{2a}$$

$$=\frac{a+12}{2}, a \neq 0$$

Multiplying Rational Expressions

ANSWERS AND SOLUTIONS

1. Simplify the expression, and multiply as necessary. The NPVs can be identified using the original denominators in factored form.

$$\left(\frac{(x+1)^3}{24x}\right)\left(\frac{6(2x)}{2x^2-2}\right)$$

$$=\left(\frac{(x+1)(x+1)(x+1)}{24\,x}\right)\left(\frac{6(2x)}{2(x-1)(x+1)}\right)$$

$$=\frac{(x+1)(x+1)}{4(x-1)}, x \neq 0,\, 1,\, -1$$

2. Simplify the expression, and multiply as necessary. The NPVs can be identified using the original denominators in factored form.

$$\left(\frac{3(x+1)^2}{4(x-1)^2}\right)\left(\frac{4(x+1)^2}{3(x-1)^2}\right)$$

$$=\left(\frac{3(x+1)(x+1)}{4(x-1)(x-1)}\right)\left(\frac{4(x+1)(x+1)}{3(x-1)(x-1)}\right)$$

$$=\frac{(x+1)^4}{(x-1)^4}, x \neq 1$$

3. **D**
Simplify the given products by eliminating common factors and using the quotient law of exponents.

$$-\left(\frac{x}{3}\right)$$

$$=-\frac{x}{3}$$

$$\left(\frac{2}{3}\right)\left(\frac{6}{x}\right)$$

$$=\frac{12}{3x}$$

$$=\frac{4}{x}, x \neq 0$$

$$\left(\frac{3}{3x}\right)(2)$$

$$=\left(\frac{3}{3x}\right)\left(\frac{2}{1}\right)$$

$$=\frac{2}{x}, x \neq 0$$

$$\left(\frac{-x}{4x^2}\right)\left(\frac{-12x}{x}\right)$$

$$=\left(\frac{-x}{4\,x^2}\right)\left(\frac{-12\,x}{x}\right)$$

$$=\frac{3}{x}, x \neq 0$$

The expression $\left(\frac{-x}{4x^2}\right)\left(\frac{-12x}{x}\right)$ is equivalent to $\frac{3}{x}$, $x \neq 0$.

4. Simplify the expression, and multiply as necessary. The NPVs can be identified using the original denominators in factored form.

$$\left(\frac{x^2-4}{x^2+5x-14}\right)\left(\frac{2x^2+14x}{2}\right)$$

$$=\left(\frac{(x-2)(x+2)}{(x-2)(x+7)}\right)\left(\frac{2x(x+7)}{2}\right)$$

$$=\left(\frac{(x-2)(x+2)}{(x-2)(x+7)}\right)\left(\frac{2x(x+7)}{2}\right)$$

$$=x(x+2), x \neq 2,\, -7$$

5. Answers will vary. The two rational expressions must simplify (after multiplication) to $\frac{2}{x}$ and should therefore be more complex than $\frac{2}{x}$ (there should be some common factors to eliminate).

An example is $\left(\frac{2(x+1)}{x}\right)\left(\frac{1}{(x+1)}\right)$.

The restrictions for this are $x \neq 0$ and $x \neq -1$.

6. Answers will vary. However, the initial denominator for one of the rational expressions must have a factor that becomes zero when $x = 4$.

An example is $\left(\frac{2(x-4)^2}{x(x-4)}\right)\left(\frac{3}{3(x-4)}\right)$ that has NPVs of $x = 0$ and $x = 4$.

7. **A**
In the given expression, the last factor in the denominator $(x+n-1)$ is one less than the last factor in the numerator $(x+n)$. As such, after reducing, all the factors in the denominator will be eliminated and the numerator will remain as $(x+n)$. There will be $(n-1)$ non-permissible values, and the denominator will be 1.

8. Simplify the expression, and multiply as necessary. The NPVs can be identified using the original denominators in factored form.

$$\frac{3x^3 + 2x^2 - 3x - 2}{x+1} \times \frac{15x}{9x^2 + 6x}$$

$$= \frac{x^2(3x+2) - 1(3x+2)}{x+1} \times \frac{15x}{3x(3x+2)}$$

$$= \frac{(x-1)\cancel{(x+1)}\cancel{(3x+2)}}{\cancel{x+1}} \times \frac{\overset{5}{\cancel{15x}}}{\cancel{3x}\cancel{(3x+2)}}$$

$$= 5(x-1), \ x \neq 0, -1, -\frac{2}{3}$$

The first numerator can be factored by grouping, which is written as $(x^2 - 1)(3x + 2)$. Since one of these factors is a difference of squares, further factoring is required.

Dividing Rational Expressions

PRACTICE EXERCISES
ANSWERS AND SOLUTIONS

1. The expression $\dfrac{5}{\left(\dfrac{20}{x^2}\right)}$ can be rewritten as $\dfrac{5}{1} \div \dfrac{20}{x^2}$

and then rewritten as the product $\left(\dfrac{5}{1}\right)\left(\dfrac{x^2}{20}\right)$.

This simplifies to $\dfrac{x^2}{4}$, $x \neq 0$.

2. Area $= \dfrac{\text{base} \times \text{height}}{2}$

$$A = \left(x^2 - 2x + 1\right)\left(\frac{2x}{x-1}\right)^2 \div 2$$

$$A = (x-1)(x-1)\left(\frac{4x^2}{(x-1)(x-1)}\right) \times \frac{1}{2}$$

$$A = \cancel{(x-1)}\cancel{(x-1)}\left(\frac{\overset{2}{\cancel{4}}x^2}{\cancel{(x-1)}\cancel{(x-1)}}\right) \times \frac{1}{\cancel{2}}$$

$$A = 2x^2, \ x \neq 1$$

3. **A**

One method for solving $\dfrac{x}{3} \div y = \dfrac{2}{x}$ is to investigate what expression must be multiplied by $\dfrac{x}{3}$ to give $\dfrac{2}{x}$. The denominator of $\dfrac{2}{x}$ is x, and the numerator of $\dfrac{x}{3}$ is x, so the unknown expression must have an x^2 in the denominator.

$$\left(\frac{x}{3}\right)\left(\frac{}{x^2}\right) = \frac{2}{x}$$

Also, the denominator of $\dfrac{x}{3}$ is 3, and the numerator of $\dfrac{2}{x}$ is 2, so the unknown expression must have a 6 in the numerator.

$$\left(\frac{x}{3}\right)\left(\frac{6}{x^2}\right) = \frac{2}{x}$$

The reciprocal of $\dfrac{6}{x^2}$ will give y for the division statement, so $y = \dfrac{x^2}{6}$ in $\dfrac{x}{3} \div y = \dfrac{2}{x}$.

$$\frac{x}{3} \div y$$

$$= \frac{x}{3} \div \frac{x^2}{6}$$

$$= \frac{x}{3} \times \frac{6}{x^2}$$

$$= \frac{2}{x}$$

4. Rewrite the quotient as a product using the reciprocal of the second expression. Simplify the product, and multiply as necessary. The NPVs can be identified using the original denominators in the quotient and the new denominator in the product.

$$\frac{x^2 - x - 12}{x+1} \div \frac{x^2 - 5x + 4}{x^2 - 1}$$

$$= \frac{(x+3)(x-4)}{x+1} \times \frac{(x-1)(x+1)}{(x-1)(x+4)}$$

$$= \frac{(x+3)\cancel{(x-4)}}{\cancel{x+1}} \times \frac{\cancel{(x-1)}\cancel{(x+1)}}{\cancel{(x-1)}\cancel{(x+4)}}$$

$$= x + 3, \ x \neq -1, 1, 4$$

5. Rewrite the quotient as a product using the reciprocal of the second expression. Simplify the product, and multiply as necessary. The NPVs can be identified using the original denominators in the quotient and the new denominator in the product.

$$\frac{4(1-x)}{x} \div \frac{x-1}{2x}$$

$$= \left(\frac{4(1-x)}{x}\right)\left(\frac{2x}{x-1}\right)$$

$$= \left(\frac{-4(\cancel{-1+x})}{\cancel{x}}\right)\left(\frac{2\cancel{x}}{\cancel{x-1}}\right)$$

$$= -8, x \neq 0, 1$$

6. Rewrite $\dfrac{25-x^2}{bx} \div \dfrac{(5+x)}{2b} \div \dfrac{(x-5)}{-(bx-1)} \times \dfrac{x^2}{(bx-1)}$

as the product of four rational expressions. Factor and eliminate any common factors.

$$\frac{25-x^2}{bx} \div \frac{(5+x)}{2b} \div \frac{(x-5)}{-(bx-1)} \cdot \frac{x^2}{(bx-1)}$$

$$= \frac{25-x^2}{bx} \cdot \frac{2b}{(5+x)} \cdot \frac{-(bx-1)}{(x-5)} \cdot \frac{x^2}{(bx-1)}$$

$$= \frac{(5-x)(5+x)}{bx} \cdot \frac{2b}{(5+x)} \cdot \frac{(bx-1)}{-(x-5)} \cdot \frac{x^2}{(bx-1)}$$

$$= \frac{(\cancel{5-x})(\cancel{5+x})}{\cancel{b}\cancel{x}} \cdot \frac{2\cancel{b}}{(\cancel{5+x})} \cdot \frac{(\cancel{bx-1})}{(\cancel{5-x})} \cdot \frac{\cancel{x^2}^{x}}{(\cancel{bx-1})}$$

$$= 2x$$

Note that the negative with $(bx-1)$ was written with $(x-5)$, which was then multiplied to give $(5-x)$.

State the NPVs and solve for b.

$bx = 0$

$\quad x = 0$

$2b = 0$

$\quad b = 0$

$(bx-1) = 0$

$\quad x = \dfrac{1}{b}$ and $b = \dfrac{1}{x}$

$(x \pm 5) = 0$

$\quad x = \pm 5$

Therefore, the NPVs for x are 0, $\dfrac{1}{b}$, 5, and -5,

and the NPVs for b are 0 and $\dfrac{1}{x}$.

Since the simplified form for this division is $2x$, any value of b that is not a restricted value (NPV) will produce this result.

7. **A**
When simplifying, it is true that common factors can disappear, but the NPVs are identified from the original denominators, so they are not lost or eliminated.

Restricted values are found only in the denominator. When an expression is replaced by its reciprocal, the new denominator can produce new restricted values. Simplifying is the process of eliminating factors that are common to the numerator and denominator. Any fraction with a denominator of zero is undefined.

Adding and Subtracting Rational Expressions

ANSWERS AND SOLUTIONS

1. **Step 1**
Identify the LCD, and write equivalent expressions with the new denominator.

The LCD is $(3x)(4)$. Note the last term has a denominator of 1.

$$\frac{2}{3x} + \frac{3x}{4} - 1$$

$$= \frac{2(4)}{(3x)(4)} + \frac{3x(3x)}{(3x)(4)} - \frac{1(3x)(4)}{(3x)(4)}$$

$$= \frac{8}{(3x)(4)} + \frac{9x^2}{(3x)(4)} - \frac{12x}{(3x)(4)}$$

Step 2
Combine like terms in the numerators, keeping the common denominator unchanged.

$$\frac{8}{(3x)(4)} + \frac{9x^2}{(3x)(4)} - \frac{12x}{(3x)(4)}$$

$$= \frac{9x^2 - 12x + 8}{12x}$$

Step 3
Check if the expression can be reduced further, and state the NPVs.

Since the numerator is not factorable, the expression is $\dfrac{9x^2 - 12x + 8}{12x}$, $x \neq 0$ in simplest form.

2. C
The original denominator in the expression $\dfrac{(x+1)(x-1)}{12x^2}$ will be multiplied by $2x$, so the new numerator will also be multiplied by $2x$.

The new numerator will be $2x(x+1)(x-1)$

or $2x\left(x^2 - 1\right)$.

3. Isolate the term with x, and combine the like terms with y.

With a single expression on either side of the equal sign, cross-multiply and solve for x.

$$\frac{9y}{4} - \frac{x}{2} = \frac{y}{4}$$
$$\frac{9y}{4} - \frac{y}{4} = \frac{x}{2}$$
$$\frac{8y}{4} = \frac{x}{2}$$
$$16y = 4x$$
$$4y = x$$

Alternate solution:
Combine the terms on the left side, and then cross-multiply. Gather like terms, and solve for x.

$$\frac{9y}{4} - \frac{x}{2} = \frac{y}{4}$$
$$\frac{9y}{4} - \frac{2x}{4} = \frac{y}{4}$$
$$\frac{9y - 2x}{4} = \frac{y}{4}$$
$$\cancel{4}(9y - 2x) = \cancel{4}(y)$$
$$-2x = y - 9y$$
$$-2x = -8y$$
$$x = 4y$$

The given solutions solve this question step by step, but at any point along the way, the solution may be stated by observation.

4. Step 1
Simplify each expression where possible.

$$\frac{a+3}{(2a+2)} + \frac{a-1}{2(a+1)} - \frac{6}{a}$$
$$= \frac{a+3}{2(a+1)} + \frac{a-1}{2(a+1)} - \frac{6}{a}$$

The expressions cannot be simplified, but the denominator of the first expression can be factored.

Step 2
Identify the lowest common denominator (LCD). The LCD will be $(2)(a)(a+1)$.

Step 3
Write an equivalent expression with the LCD as the denominator.
$$\frac{a+3}{2(a+1)} + \frac{a-1}{2(a+1)} - \frac{6}{a}$$
$$= \frac{(a+3)(a)}{(2)(a)(a+1)} + \frac{(a-1)(a)}{(2)(a)(a+1)} - \frac{6(2)(a+1)}{(2)(a)(a+1)}$$
$$= \frac{a^2 + 3a}{(2)(a)(a+1)} + \frac{a^2 - a}{(2)(a)(a+1)} - \frac{12a + 12}{(2)(a)(a+1)}$$

Step 4
Combine like terms in the numerators, keeping the common denominator unchanged.
$$\frac{a^2 + 3a}{(2)(a)(a+1)} + \frac{a^2 - a}{(2)(a)(a+1)} - \frac{12a + 12}{(2)(a)(a+1)}$$
$$= \frac{a^2 + 3a + a^2 - a - 12a - 12}{(2)(a)(a+1)}$$
$$= \frac{2a^2 - 10a - 12}{(2)(a)(a+1)}$$

Step 5
Check if the expression can be reduced further, and state the NPVs.
$$\frac{2a^2 - 10a - 12}{(2)(a)(a+1)}$$
$$= \frac{\cancel{2}\left(a^2 - 5a - 6\right)}{\left(\cancel{2}\right)(a)(a+1)}$$
$$= \frac{(a-6)\cancel{(a+1)}}{(a)\cancel{(a+1)}}$$
$$= \frac{(a-6)}{a}, \; a \neq 0, -1$$

5. **Step 1**

Simplify each expression where possible.

$$\frac{x^2-6x-7}{x+1}-\frac{2x+12}{2x+2}+\frac{x+1}{x^2-1}$$

$$=\frac{(x+1)(x-7)}{(x+1)}-\frac{\cancel{2}(x+6)}{\cancel{2}(x+1)}+\frac{(x+1)}{(x+1)(x-1)}$$

The first and third expressions can be reduced by eliminating the common factors of $(x+1)$.

However, by noting the denominators of all three expressions, it can be seen that a common denominator is going to include $(x+1)$ as a factor, so simplifying is not necessary. A factor of 2 can be eliminated in the second expression.

Step 2

Identify the lowest common denominator (LCD). The LCD will be $(x+1)(x-1)$.

Step 3

Write an equivalent expression with the LCD as the denominator.

$$\frac{(x+1)(x-7)}{(x+1)}-\frac{(x+6)}{(x+1)}+\frac{(x+1)}{(x+1)(x-1)}$$

$$=\frac{(x-1)(x+1)(x-7)}{(x+1)(x-1)}-\frac{(x+6)(x-1)}{(x+1)(x-1)}+\frac{(x+1)}{(x+1)(x-1)}$$

$$=\frac{(x^2-1)(x-7)}{(x+1)(x-1)}-\frac{(x^2+5x-6)}{(x+1)(x-1)}+\frac{x+1}{(x+1)(x-1)}$$

$$=\frac{x^3-7x^2-x+7}{(x+1)(x-1)}-\frac{x^2+5x-6}{(x+1)(x-1)}+\frac{x+1}{(x+1)(x-1)}$$

Step 4

Combine like terms in the numerators, keeping the common denominator unchanged.

$$\frac{x^3-7x^2-x+7}{(x+1)(x-1)}-\frac{x^2+5x-6}{(x+1)(x-1)}+\frac{x+1}{(x+1)(x-1)}$$

$$=\frac{x^3-7x^2-x+7-x^2-5x+6+x+1}{(x+1)(x-1)}$$

$$=\frac{x^3-8x^2-5x+14}{(x+1)(x-1)}$$

Step 5

Check if the expression can be reduced further, and state the NPVs.

The expression is in simplest form since it cannot be factored further. The NPVs are $x=1$ and $x=-1$, which can be written beside the expression as $\frac{x^3-8x^2-5x+14}{(x+1)(x-1)}, x\neq 1,-1$.

6. **Step 1**

Simplify each expression where possible.

$$\frac{2}{(1-x)}+\frac{x-1}{(x-1)(x)}-\frac{3}{(x-1)(x)}$$

$$=\frac{-2}{(x-1)}+\frac{x-1}{(x-1)(x)}-\frac{3}{(x-1)(x)}$$

The second expression can be reduced by eliminating the common factor of $(x-1)$.

However, by noting the denominators of all three expressions, it can be seen that a common denominator is going to include $(x-1)$ as a factor, so simplifying is not necessary. A factor of -1 can be eliminated in the first expression, leaving the denominator as $(x-1)$.

Step 2

Identify the lowest common denominator (LCD). The LCD will be $x(x-1)$.

Step 3

Write an equivalent expression with the LCD as the denominator.

$$\frac{-2}{(x-1)}+\frac{x-1}{(x-1)(x)}-\frac{3}{(x-1)(x)}$$

$$=\frac{-2(x)}{(x-1)(x)}+\frac{x-1}{(x-1)(x)}-\frac{3}{(x-1)(x)}$$

Step 4

Combine like terms in the numerators, keeping the common denominator unchanged.

$$\frac{-2(x)}{(x-1)(x)}+\frac{x-1}{(x-1)(x)}-\frac{3}{(x-1)(x)}$$

$$=\frac{-2x+x-1-3}{(x-1)(x)}$$

$$=\frac{-x-4}{(x-1)(x)}, x\neq 0,1$$

For the numerator to equal -3, set it equal to -3 and solve for x.

$$-x-4=-3$$
$$-4+3=x$$
$$-1=x$$

Therefore, the value of x must be -1 for the numerator to equal -3.

Rational Equations and Problem Solving

ANSWERS AND SOLUTIONS

1. **Step 1**
With a single expression on either side of the equal sign, cross-multiply to remove the denominators, and then expand where necessary.
$$\frac{2}{x-1} = \frac{3}{x}$$
$$2(x) = 3(x-1)$$
$$2x = 3x - 3$$

Step 2
Gather like terms, and solve for x.
$$2x = 3x - 3$$
$$3 = x$$

Step 3
State any NPVs for the variable.

The NPVs from the original equation $\frac{2}{x-1} = \frac{3}{x}$ are

$x = 1$ and $x = 0$.

Therefore, the solution is $x = 3$.

2. **Step 1**
With a single expression on either side of the equal sign, cross-multiply to remove the denominators, and then expand where necessary.
$$\frac{3x+1}{6x} = \frac{x+1}{2x+1}$$
$$(3x+1)(2x+1) = (x+1)(6x)$$
$$6x^2 + 5x + 1 = 6x^2 + 6x$$

Step 2
Gather like terms, and solve for x.
$$\cancel{6x^2} + 5x + 1 = \cancel{6x^2} + 6x$$
$$1 = x$$

Step 3
State any NPVs for the variable.

The NPVs from the original equation
$\frac{3x+1}{6x} = \frac{x+1}{2x+1}$ are $x = 0$ and $x = -\frac{1}{2}$.

Therefore, the solution is $x = 1$.

3. **Step 1**
Simplify where possible.
$$\frac{x}{x+1} = \frac{-2}{2x+2}$$
$$\frac{x}{x+1} = \frac{\cancel{-2}^{-1}}{\cancel{2}(x+1)}$$
$$\frac{x}{x+1} = \frac{-1}{x+1}$$

After factoring and eliminating a factor of 2 from the second expression, it is possible to continue solving using the set steps or to solve by observation.

Since both denominators are the same, the numerators must also be equal for the equality to be true. This means that $x = -1$. However, by noting the NPVs, it is found that $x \neq -1$. The only solution to this equation is non-permissible, so there are no solutions.

4. **Step 1**
Determine the LCM and the NPVs.

For the expression $\frac{2}{x} - \frac{5}{3x} = 4$, the LCM of the denominators is $3x$. The only NPV is $x = 0$.

Step 2
Multiply each term by the LCM.
$$\frac{2}{x} - \frac{5}{3x} = 4$$
$$(3x)\left[\frac{2}{x} - \frac{5}{3x} = 4\right]$$
$$(3x)\frac{2}{x} - (3x)\frac{5}{3x} = (3x)4$$

Step 3
Simplify and solve for x.
$$(3\cancel{x})\frac{2}{\cancel{x}} - (\cancel{3x})\frac{5}{\cancel{3x}} = (3x)4$$
$$6 - 5 = 12x$$
$$1 = 12x$$
$$\frac{1}{12} = x$$
$$x = \frac{1}{12}, x \neq 0$$

5. B

Solve by cross-multiplying.

$$\frac{13}{y+1} = 4, \; y \neq -1$$
$$13 = 4(y+1)$$
$$13 = 4y + 4$$
$$9 = 4y$$
$$y = \frac{9}{4}$$

The NPV from the original equation $\frac{13}{y+1} = 4$ is

$y \neq -1$. Therefore, the solution is $y = \frac{9}{4}$.

Alternative Solution

Use verification with each value to see if the left side equals the right side of the equation.

$y = \dfrac{3}{2}$	
$\dfrac{13}{\left(\dfrac{3}{2}\right)+1}$	4
$\dfrac{13}{\left(\dfrac{5}{2}\right)}$	4
$\dfrac{26}{5}$	4

$y = \dfrac{9}{4}$	
$\dfrac{13}{\left(\dfrac{9}{4}\right)+1}$	4
$\dfrac{13}{\left(\dfrac{13}{4}\right)}$	4
4	4

$y = \dfrac{4}{9}$	
$\dfrac{13}{\left(\dfrac{4}{9}\right)+1}$	4
$\dfrac{13}{\left(\dfrac{13}{9}\right)}$	4
9	4

$y = \dfrac{2}{3}$	
$\dfrac{13}{\left(\dfrac{2}{3}\right)+1}$	4
$\dfrac{13}{\left(\dfrac{5}{3}\right)}$	4
$\dfrac{39}{5}$	4

6. A cube has three equal dimensions (length, width, and height), and its volume is determined by multiplying these three dimensions together.

Step 1

Assign a variable to represent the unknown, and set up an equation using the given information.

Let x represent the side length of the small cube. This means the side length of the large cube, being twice as long, will be $2x$.

Since you are given the total volume of the two halves, make an equation that represents this total. Specifically, half of the small cube's volume added to half of the large cube's volume will equal 36 cm^3.

The volume of the small cube will be $V = lwh$ or $V_{small\;cube} = x^3$ since the three dimensions are equal. The large cube will have a volume of $V_{large\;cube} = (2x)^3$.

$$\frac{V_{small\;cube}}{2} + \frac{V_{large\;cube}}{2} = 36$$
$$\frac{x^3}{2} + \frac{(2x)^3}{2} = 36$$
$$\frac{x^3}{2} + \frac{8x^3}{2} = 36$$

Step 2

Solve the rational equation.

Simplify the left side, and then solve for x.

$$\frac{x^3}{2} + \frac{8x^3}{2} = 36$$
$$\frac{9x^3}{2} = 36$$
$$9x^3 = 72$$
$$x^3 = 8$$
$$x = 2$$

The side length of the small cube is 2 cm. There are no non-permissible values to check.

Topic Practice Questions

ANSWERS AND SOLUTIONS

1. D

The expression $\dfrac{4}{2x-2}$ simplifies to the expression

$\dfrac{2}{(x-1)}$ through factoring and eliminating a

common factor of 2.

The other answers reflect some common mistakes in simplifying.

2. Factor where possible, and eliminate common factors to simplify the expression.

The NPVs can be identified using the original denominator in factored form.

$$\frac{2x^2 - x - 1}{(6x+3)}$$
$$= \frac{(2x+1)(x-1)}{3(2x+1)}$$
$$= \frac{x-1}{3}, x \neq -\frac{1}{2}$$

3. **D**
After factoring, the original denominator will be $2(a)(a-1)$, so $a \neq 0$ and $a \neq 1$.

The variable x need not be introduced. Eliminating common factors does not eliminate the need to list NPVs from the original denominator.

4. **Step 1**
Find expressions for the lengths of rectangles A and B.

If the area of a rectangular object is found by multiplying the length and width $(A = lw)$, then rearranging this formula for length gives the formula $l = \dfrac{A}{w}$.

$$l_A = \frac{A_A}{w_A} \qquad\qquad l_B = \frac{A_B}{w_B}$$
$$l_A = \frac{x^2 + 4x - 5}{x-1} \qquad l_B = \frac{x^2 - 4}{x-2}$$

Step 2
Write a rational expression of the form $l_A \div l_B$, and simplify.
$$l_A \div l_B$$
$$= \frac{x^2+4x-5}{x-1} \div \frac{x^2-4}{x-2}$$
$$= \frac{(x-1)(x+5)}{x-1} \times \frac{(x-2)}{(x-2)(x+2)}$$
$$= \frac{(x+5)}{(x+2)}$$

Step 3
Identify the NPVs.

Considering each denominator before and after any simplifying, $x \neq 1$, $x \neq 2$, and $x \neq -2$. However, these rectangles would not exist in real space if either the length or width were reduced to zero or a negative value. Considering that the width of rectangle A is $(x-1)$ and the width of rectangle B is $(x-2)$, then no value of the variable less than or equal to 2 should be allowed. The full set of restrictions for the variable would then become $x > 2$.

5. Rewrite the quotient as a product using the reciprocal of the second expression.

Simplify the product and multiply as necessary. The NPVs can be identified using the original denominators in the quotient and the new denominator in the product.
$$\frac{(x+2)(x-3)}{(x-a)^2} \div \frac{x^2 - x - 6}{x-1}$$
$$= \left(\frac{(x+2)(x-3)}{(x-a)^2}\right)\left(\frac{x-1}{x^2-x-6}\right)$$
$$= \left(\frac{(x+2)(x-3)}{(x-a)(x-a)}\right)\left(\frac{x-1}{(x+2)(x-3)}\right)$$
$$= \frac{x-1}{(x-a)(x-a)}, x \neq -2, 3$$

For the numerator to simplify to 1, there must be a common factor in the denominator to cancel the $(x-1)$ remaining in the numerator. This means that the denominator is $(x-1)^2$, and $a = 1$.

The expression then simplifies to $\dfrac{1}{(x-1)}$, where $x \neq 1$, $x \neq -2$, and $x \neq 3$. Since a is not x, $a = 1$ is allowed even though $x \neq 1$.

6. **Step 1**
Simplify each expression where possible.
$$\frac{3}{x^2+2x} + \frac{x-1}{3x} - \frac{x^2+7x+10}{3x^2+15x}$$
$$= \frac{3}{x(x+2)} + \frac{x-1}{3x} - \frac{(x+5)(x+2)}{3x(x+5)}$$

97

Step 2
Identify the lowest common denominator (LCD).
The LCD will be $3x(x+2)$.

Step 3
Write an equivalent expression with the LCD as the denominator.

$$\frac{3}{x(x+2)}+\frac{x-1}{3x}-\frac{(x+5)(x+2)}{3x(x+5)}$$

$$=\frac{3(3)}{3x(x+2)}+\frac{(x-1)(x+2)}{3x(x+2)}-\frac{(x+2)(x+2)}{3x(x+2)}$$

$$=\frac{9}{3x(x+2)}+\frac{x^2+x-2}{3x(x+2)}-\frac{x^2+4x+4}{3x(x+2)}$$

Step 4
Combine like terms in the numerators, keeping the common denominator unchanged.

$$\frac{9}{3x(x+2)}+\frac{x^2+x-2}{3x(x+2)}-\frac{x^2+4x+4}{3x(x+2)}$$

$$=\frac{9+x^2+x-2-x^2-4x-4}{3x(x+2)}$$

$$=\frac{-3x+3}{3x(x+2)}$$

Step 5
Check if the expression can be reduced further, and state the NPVs.

$$\frac{-3x+3}{3x(x+2)}$$

$$=\frac{3(-x+1)}{3x(x+2)}$$

$$=\frac{-x+1}{x(x+2)}, x\neq 0,-2,-5$$

7. **Step 1**
Assign a variable to represent the unknown, and set up an equation using the given information.

Let x represent the unknown number. Set up an equation using the information that half of an unknown number is added to one quarter of the original unknown number, with the result equal to 10.

$$\frac{1}{2} \text{ of unknown} +\frac{1}{4} \text{ of unknown} = 10$$

$$\frac{x}{2}+\frac{x}{4}=10$$

Step 2
Solve the rational equation.

Multiply the equation by the LCM to eliminate the denominators, and then solve for x.

$$\frac{x}{2}+\frac{x}{4}=10$$

$$(4)\left[\frac{x}{2}+\frac{x}{4}=10\right]$$

$$(\overset{2}{\cancel{4}})\frac{x}{\cancel{2}}+(\cancel{4})\frac{x}{\cancel{4}}=(4)10$$

$$2x+x=40$$

$$3x=40$$

$$x=\frac{40}{3}$$

Expressed as a fraction, the original number is $\frac{40}{3}$.

Step 3
Verify the solution.

One half of $\frac{40}{3}$ is $\frac{20}{3}$.

One quarter of $\frac{40}{3}$ is $\frac{10}{3}$.

Added together, these equal $\frac{30}{3}$, or 10, so the answer is verified.

8. **Step 1**
Assign a variable to represent the unknown, and set up an equation using the given information.

Let x represent the minimum mark that Molly must achieve on her sixth test.

To set up an equation, the test scores could each be written out as a series of fractions (representing the percentage marks) with the unknown included. For a desired passing grade, the overall average needs to be 50%, which can be represented by a mark of $\frac{50}{100}$ on each of the six tests. There are several different approaches that could be used to solve this type of question.

$$\frac{50}{100}+\frac{50}{100}+\frac{50}{100}+\frac{50}{100}+\frac{52}{100}+\frac{x}{100}=\frac{50(6)}{100}$$

Step 2
Solve the rational equation.

Simplify the left side, and then cross-multiply to solve for x.

$$\frac{50}{100}+\frac{50}{100}+\frac{50}{100}+\frac{50}{100}+\frac{52}{100}+\frac{x}{100}=\frac{50(6)}{100}$$

$$\frac{252+x}{100}=\frac{300}{100}$$

$$\left(\cancel{100}\right)(252+x)=\left(\cancel{100}\right)(300)$$

$$252+x=300$$

$$x=48$$

Therefore, Molly must achieve a minimum mark of 48% on the sixth test to receive an overall passing grade.

TRIGONOMETRY

The Primary Trigonometric Ratios and Special Triangles

ANSWERS AND SOLUTIONS

1. Since the adjacent side to θ and the hypotenuse are known, use the cosine ratio.

$$\cos\theta=\frac{24}{37}$$

$$\theta=\cos^{-1}\left(\frac{24}{37}\right)$$

$$\theta\doteq49.6°$$

2. **Step 1**
Draw a diagram that represents the known information.

If $\tan\theta=\dfrac{12}{5}$, then the opposite and adjacent sides to θ are known.

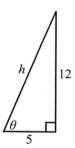

Step 2
Use the Pythagorean theorem to find the missing side length, h.

$$h^2=12^2+5^2$$

$$h=\sqrt{12^2+5^2}$$

$$h=\sqrt{169}$$

$$h=13$$

Step 3
Find $\cos\theta$.

Therefore, $\cos\theta=\dfrac{5}{13}$.

3. Since side x is opposite the given angle, and the hypotenuse is known, use the sine ratio.

$$\sin 52° = \frac{x}{15}$$
$$15\sin 52° = x$$
$$11.8 \text{ cm} \doteq x$$

4. Use the 45-45-90 and the 30-60-90 triangles and the primary trigonometric ratios:

$$\sin \theta = \frac{\text{opposite}}{\text{hypotenuse}}$$
$$\cos \theta = \frac{\text{adjacent}}{\text{hypotenuse}}$$
$$\tan \theta = \frac{\text{opposite}}{\text{adjacent}}$$

	$\sin \theta$	$\cos \theta$	$\tan \theta$
$\theta = 30°$	$\dfrac{1}{2}$	$\dfrac{\sqrt{3}}{2}$	$\dfrac{1}{\sqrt{3}} = \dfrac{\sqrt{3}}{3}$
$\theta = 45°$	$\dfrac{1}{\sqrt{2}} = \dfrac{\sqrt{2}}{2}$	$\dfrac{1}{\sqrt{2}} = \dfrac{\sqrt{2}}{2}$	1
$\theta = 60°$	$\dfrac{\sqrt{3}}{2}$	$\dfrac{1}{2}$	$\sqrt{3}$

Angles in Standard Position

ANSWERS AND SOLUTIONS

1. **Step 1**
    Draw the rotation angle in standard position, and identify the quadrant in which it terminates.

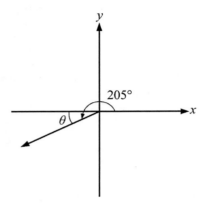

The rotation angle 205° terminates in quadrant III.

Step 2
Find the reference angle.

Let θ represent the reference angle. In quadrant III, the reference angle is equal to the rotation angle minus 180°.
$$\theta = 205° - 180°$$
$$= 25°$$

The reference angle is 25°.

2. **Step 1**
    Identify the quadrant in which the terminal arm of the rotation angle lies. Use the CAST rule to identify if the ratio is positive or negative.

    The rotation angle 240° terminates in quadrant III, so the cosine ratio will be negative.

    Step 2
    Find the reference angle.

    In quadrant III, the reference angle is equal to the rotation angle minus 180°.
    $$240° - 180° = 60°$$

Step 3
Use the reference angle and related special triangle to find the exact value.
$$\cos 240°$$
$$= -\cos 60°$$
$$= -\left(\frac{1}{2}\right)$$
$$= -\frac{1}{2}$$

The exact value of cos 240° is $-\frac{1}{2}$.

3. **Step 1**
Since point $P(12, -5)$ is already sketched in quadrant IV, it is known that $x = 12$ and $y = -5$.

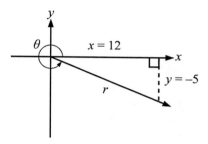

Step 2
Find the length of r using the Pythagorean theorem. The radius is always positive because it is a length (not a coordinate).
$$r = \sqrt{12^2 + (-5)^2}$$
$$r = \sqrt{169}$$
$$r = 13$$

Step 3
Find the primary trigonometric ratios.

Keep the CAST rule in mind to determine the sign of each.
$$\sin\theta = \frac{y}{r} = -\frac{5}{13}$$
$$\cos\theta = \frac{x}{r} = \frac{12}{13}$$
$$\tan\theta = \frac{y}{x} = -\frac{5}{12}$$

4. The angle 210° terminates in quadrant III, so it has a reference angle of $210° - 180° = 30°$, and the cosine ratio will be negative.

Using a special triangle, the exact value of cos 210° in quadrant III is $-\frac{\sqrt{3}}{2}$. The cosine ratio is also negative in quadrant II. Therefore, the rotation angle with the same cosine ratio as 210° will be a quadrant II angle with a reference angle of 30°. The rotation angle in quadrant II will be $180° - 30° = 150°$.

Therefore, 150° is the other angle that has the same cosine ratio as 210°, where $0° \le \theta < 360°$.

5. **Step 1**
Use the CAST rule to identify the two quadrants in which the sine ratio is positive.

The sine ratio is positive in quadrants I and II.

Step 2
Find the reference angle using the inverse sine function on a calculator.
$$\theta = \sin^{-1}(0.7071)$$
$$\doteq 45°$$

Step 3
Find the two rotation angles.

In quadrant I, the rotation angle is equal to the reference angle. In quadrant II, the rotation angle is $180° - 45° = 135°$.

Therefore, $\sin 45° = 0.7071$ and $\sin 135° = 0.7071$.

6. **Step 1**
Use the CAST rule to identify the two quadrants in which the tangent ratio is positive.

Since the tangent ratio is positive, the rotation angles will be in quadrants I and III.

Step 2
Find the reference angle using the 45-45-90 special triangle.

Using the 45-45-90 special triangle, the tangent ratio of 1 corresponds to a reference angle of 45°.

Step 3
Find the two rotation angles.

The rotation angles are $\theta = 45°$ and $\theta = 180° + 45°$, which is $\theta = 225°$.

The Sine Law

ANSWERS AND SOLUTIONS

1. The complete ratio $\dfrac{25}{\sin 50°}$ is known, and the angle opposite side x is 83°. Substitute these values into the sine law, and solve for x.

$$\frac{x}{\sin 83°} = \frac{25}{\sin 50°}$$
$$x = \frac{25\sin(83°)}{\sin 50°}$$
$$x \doteq 32.4 \text{ m}$$

2. The complete ratio $\dfrac{\sin 81°}{55}$ is known, and the side opposite θ is 32 m. Substitute these values into the sine law, and solve for θ.

$$\frac{\sin \theta}{32} = \frac{\sin 81°}{55}$$
$$\sin \theta = \frac{32\sin(81°)}{55}$$
$$\theta = \sin^{-1}\left(\frac{32\sin(81°)}{55}\right)$$
$$\theta \doteq 35°$$

3. Do not use the primary trigonometric ratios since you cannot be sure that either triangle has a right angle.

    Step 1
    Solve for side x.

    Find side x first since the complete ratio $\dfrac{52}{\sin 68°}$ is known and the angle opposite side x is 56°.

$$\frac{x}{\sin 56°} = \frac{52}{\sin 68°}$$
$$x = \frac{52\sin(56°)}{\sin 68°}$$
$$x \doteq 46.4956$$

    Step 2
    Solve for θ.

    Now that the length of side x is known, solve for θ.

$$\frac{\sin \theta}{46.4956} \doteq \frac{\sin 42°}{41}$$
$$\sin \theta \doteq \frac{46.4956\sin(42°)}{41}$$
$$\theta \doteq \sin^{-1}\left(\frac{46.4956\sin(42°)}{41}\right)$$
$$\theta \doteq 49.36°$$

Therefore, side x is 46 m and θ is 49°.

4. **Step 1**
    Find the missing angle.
    Find $\angle Z$ to create a complete ratio.
    $$\angle Z = 180° - 100° - 50°$$
    $$= 30°$$

    The complete set is $\dfrac{25}{\sin 30°}$.

    Step 2
    Solve for the unknown.

    The measure of $\angle Y = 50°$, which is opposite the unknown side XZ. Substitute the known values into the sine law, and solve for the length of side XZ. Side XZ could also be called side y.

$$\frac{XZ}{\sin 50°} = \frac{25}{\sin 30°}$$
$$XZ = \frac{25\sin(50°)}{\sin 30°}$$
$$XZ \doteq 38.3 \text{ m}$$

The length of side XZ is 38.3 m.

The Cosine Law

ANSWERS AND SOLUTIONS

1. To find the unknown side, use the cosine law since SAS is known.

2. Since the side opposite the unknown angle is given and a complete side-angle ratio is known, use the sine law.

3. To find the unknown angle, use the cosine law since SSS is known.

4. Since the angle opposite the unknown side can be found by subtracting the two known angles from 180° and a complete side-angle ratio is known, use the sine law.

5. **Step 1**
Label the unknown sides as x and y.

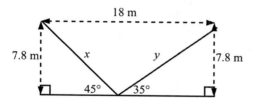

The heights of the right triangles in the diagram are both $8.3 \text{ m} - 0.5 \text{ m} = 7.8 \text{ m}$.

Step 2
Find the length of the unknown sides.

Since both sides are part of right triangles, a primary trigonometric ratio can be used to solve for x and y.

$$\sin 45° = \frac{7.8}{x}$$
$$x = \frac{7.8}{\sin 45°}$$
$$x \doteq 11.0309 \text{ m}$$
$$\sin 35° = \frac{7.8}{y}$$
$$y = \frac{7.8}{\sin 35°}$$
$$y \doteq 13.5989 \text{ m}$$

Step 3
Solve for the angle formed between the two kite strings.

Since all three sides are known, the cosine law can be used.

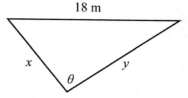

$$\cos\theta = \frac{x^2 + y^2 - 18^2}{2xy}$$

$$\theta = \cos^{-1}\left(\frac{\left(\frac{7.8}{\sin 45°}\right)^2 + \left(\frac{7.8}{\sin 35°}\right)^2 - 18^2}{2\left(\frac{7.8}{\sin 45°}\right)\left(\frac{7.8}{\sin 35°}\right)}\right)$$

$$\theta \doteq 93.3°$$

Rather than using the decimal approximations for sides x and y, the exact ratios are used to avoid any rounding errors.

Therefore, the angle formed between the two kite strings is 93.3°.

Topic Practice Questions

ANSWERS AND SOLUTIONS

1. **Step 1**
Draw a diagram that represents the information.

If $\sin\theta = \dfrac{7}{25}$, then the hypotenuse of the triangle could be 25 units, and the side opposite to θ could be 7 units (or any values that produce a ratio equivalent to $\dfrac{7}{25}$).

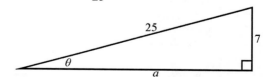

Step 2
Use the Pythagorean theorem to find a.
$$a^2 + 7^2 = 25^2$$
$$a^2 + 49 = 625$$
$$a^2 = 576$$
$$a = \sqrt{576}$$
$$a = 24$$

Step 3
Identify the required ratio now that all three sides are known.
$$\cos\theta = \frac{24}{25}$$

2. **Step 1**
Identify the reference angle.

The rotation angle terminates in quadrant IV, so the reference angle is $360° - 315° = 45°$.

Step 2
Use the 45-45-90 special triangle to find the exact value of the cosine ratio. Use the CAST rule to determine if the cosine ratio is positive or negative in quadrant IV.

The cosine ratio is positive in quadrant IV.
$$\cos 315° = \cos 45°$$
$$= \frac{1}{\sqrt{2}}$$
$$= \frac{\sqrt{2}}{2}$$

3. The coordinates of point P are given as $P(0, 14)$,

and it is known that $\sin\theta = \frac{y}{r}$, $\cos\theta = \frac{x}{r}$,

and $\tan\theta = \frac{y}{x}$.

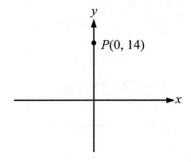

Since the terminal arm happens to be a vertical line, the radius and side y coincide (both are 14 units), and there is no reference angle. To find

the value of $\sin\theta$, $\cos\theta$, and $\tan\theta$, substitute the known information into the definition of each primary trigonometric ratio.

$$\sin\theta = \frac{y}{r} \qquad\qquad \cos\theta = \frac{x}{r}$$
$$\sin\theta = \frac{14}{14} \qquad\qquad \cos\theta = \frac{0}{14}$$
$$\sin\theta = 1 \qquad\qquad \cos\theta = 0$$

$$\tan\theta = \frac{y}{x}$$
$$\tan\theta = \frac{14}{0}$$
$$\tan\theta = \text{undefined}$$

4. **Step 1**
If necessary, make a sketch to identify the quadrant in which the rotation angle terminates.

If $\tan\theta = \frac{y}{x}$ and it is given that $\tan\theta = \frac{2}{7}$,

where θ terminates in quadrant III, then possible values for x and y are $x = -7$ and $y = -2$. This is enough information to sketch angle θ in standard position in quadrant III.

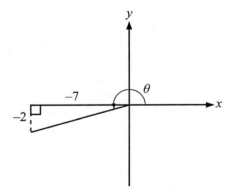

Step 2
Find the unknown ratio.

Keep the CAST rule in mind to determine the sign.

If $\sin\theta = \frac{y}{r}$, it is necessary to determine the value of r using the Pythagorean theorem.
$$r^2 = x^2 + y^2$$
$$r = \sqrt{(-7)^2 + (-2)^2}$$
$$r = \sqrt{53}$$

Therefore, $\sin\theta = \frac{-2}{\sqrt{53}}$ or $-\frac{2\sqrt{53}}{53}$.

104

5. D

Step 1
Use the CAST rule to identify the two quadrants in which the cosine ratio is negative.

The cosine ratio is negative in quadrants II and III.

Step 2
Find the reference angle using the inverse cosine function on a calculator.
$$\theta = \cos^{-1}\left(\frac{3}{5}\right)$$
$$\doteq 53°$$

Step 3
Find the two rotation angles.

In quadrant II, the rotation angle is
$180° - 53° = 127°$.

In quadrant III, the rotation angle is
$180° + 53° = 233°$.

Therefore, $\cos 127° = -\dfrac{3}{5}$ and $\cos 233° = -\dfrac{3}{5}$.

6. Step 1
Use the CAST rule to identify the two quadrants in which the ratios are both positive or both negative.

Sine and cosine are positive in quadrant I and negative in quadrant III.

Step 2
Identify the reference angle.

For $\sin\theta = \cos\theta$, the values of x and y must be the same. If this is the case, then the special 45-45-90 triangle applies in which $x = 1$ and $y = 1$. Therefore, the reference angle is 45°.

Step 3
Find the two rotation angles.

In quadrant I, the rotation angle is equal to the reference angle (45°).

In quadrant III, the rotation angle is
$180° + 45° = 225°$.

Therefore, $\sin\theta = \cos\theta$ when $\theta = 45°$ and $\theta = 225°$.

7. Step 1
Isolate $\tan\theta$.

In this case, add 1 to both sides and then divide both sides by 5.
$$5\tan\theta - 1 = 3$$
$$5\tan\theta = 4$$
$$\tan\theta = \frac{4}{5}$$

Step 2
Find the reference angle using the inverse tangent function on a calculator.
$$\theta = \tan^{-1}\left(\frac{4}{5}\right)$$
$$\doteq 38.7°$$

Step 3
Find the two rotation angles.

The tangent ratio is positive in quadrants I and III. In quadrant I, the rotation angle is equal to the reference angle (38.7°).

In quadrant III, the rotation angle is
$180° + 38.7° = 218.7°$.

Therefore, $\theta = 38.7°$ and $\theta = 218.7°$.

8. B
The primary trigonometric ratios (SOH CAH TOA) can only be used to find side or angle measures of right triangles. Therefore, the formula
$$\tan A = \frac{\text{opposite}}{\text{adjacent}}$$ works only with right triangles.
The sine law and cosine law can be used for any type of triangle.

9. Step 1
Draw a diagram representing the given information.

Assuming the ground is horizontal and the building is vertical, a right angle is formed. An angle of elevation is the measure of an angle between a horizontal ray and the one above it.

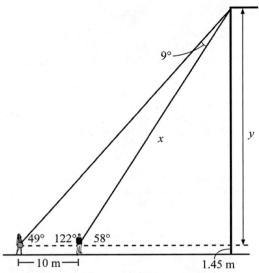

Since the angle measure of a straight line is 180°, the 122° angle can be determined by $180° - 58° = 122°$.

Step 2
Solve for side x.

Find side x first since the complete ratio $\dfrac{10}{\sin 9°}$ is known and the angle opposite to side x is 49°.

$$\frac{x}{\sin 49°} = \frac{10}{\sin 9°}$$
$$x = \frac{10\sin(49°)}{\sin 9°}$$
$$x \doteq 48.2445 \text{ m}$$

Step 3
Solve for y.

In the right triangle, side y is opposite 58°, and now the length of x, the hypotenuse, is known. Therefore, use the sine ratio.

$$\sin 58° = \frac{y}{x}$$
$$\sin 58° = \frac{y}{\left(\dfrac{10\sin(49°)}{\sin 9°}\right)}$$
$$y = \frac{10\sin(49°)\sin(58°)}{\sin(9°)}$$
$$y \doteq 40.91 \text{ m}$$

Step 4
Find the height of the tower.

The height of the student's eye level must be added to the value of y.

$$40.91 + 1.45 = 42.36$$

The height of the tower is 42.36 m.

10. Step 1
Decide which type of trigonometric law to use.

The given information is of the form SSS, so substitute the given values into the cosine law.
$$\cos\theta = \frac{18^2 + 12^2 - 19^2}{2(18)(12)}$$

Step 2
Simplify the right side, and then take the inverse cosine of both sides to solve for θ.
$$\cos\theta = \frac{107}{432}$$
$$\theta = \cos^{-1}\left(\frac{107}{432}\right)$$
$$\theta \doteq 76°$$

11. Step 1
Draw and label a possible sketch of $\triangle QRS$, where h represents the height of the triangle.

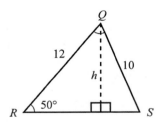

Triangle QRS has known side lengths of r and s and a known angle measure, $\angle R$, which is a non-included angle (not between sides r and s).

As such, this may be an example of an ambiguous-case triangle (SSA).

Step 2
Find the value of h.
$$\sin R = \frac{h}{s}$$
$$\sin 50° = \frac{h}{12}$$
$$12\sin 50° = h$$
$$9.2 \text{ cm} \doteq h$$

Step 3
Find the number of possible triangles.

Since side r (10 cm) is less than side s (12 cm), but greater than h (9.2 cm), there are two possible triangles and thus two possible angle measures for $\angle Q$.

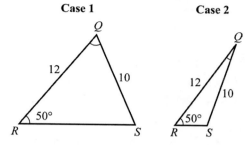

Case 1   Case 2

Step 4
Apply the sine law to calculate the measure of $\angle S$.

Substitute 10 for r, 12 for s, and 50° for $\angle R$.
$$\frac{\sin S}{12} = \frac{\sin 50°}{10}$$
$$\sin S = \frac{12\sin(50°)}{10}$$
$$S = \sin^{-1}\left(\frac{12\sin(50°)}{10}\right)$$
$$S \doteq 66.8172°$$

Since the value of $\sin S$ is positive in either quadrant I, $0° < S < 90°$, or quadrant II, $90° < S < 180°$, the measure of $\angle S$ could either be that of an acute or an obtuse angle.

Therefore, the possible measures of $\angle S$ are 66.8° or $\angle S \doteq 180° - 66.8°$, which is $\angle S \doteq 113.2°$.

Step 5
Determine the possible measures for $\angle Q$.

The sum of the angles in any triangle is 180°, so $\angle Q + \angle R + \angle S = 180°$. Since there are two possible measures for $\angle S$, there are also two possible measures for $\angle Q$.

If $\angle S \doteq 66.8°$, find the value of $\angle Q$.
$$\angle Q \doteq 180° - 50° - 66.8°$$
$$\doteq 63.2°$$

If $\angle S \doteq 113.2°$, find the value of $\angle Q$.
$$\angle Q \doteq 180° - 50° - 113.2°$$
$$\doteq 16.8°$$
To the nearest tenth of a degree, the measure of $\angle Q$ can be either 63.2° or 16.8°.

FACTORING POLYNOMIALS

Factoring Using Decomposition

ANSWERS AND SOLUTIONS

1. In $x^2 + 3x - 40$, the constant term is –40 and the middle term has a coefficient of 3.

Step 1
Find two integers with a product of –40 and a sum of 3.

The pairs of integers with a product of –40 and their respective sums are as follows:

Product	Sum
$(-1) \times 40 = -40$	$(-1) + 40 = 39$
$(-2) \times 20 = -40$	$(-2) + 20 = 18$
$(-4) \times 10 = -40$	$(-4) + 10 = 6$
$\boxed{(-5) \times 8 = -40}$	$\boxed{(-5) + 8 = 3}$
$1 \times (-40) = -40$	$1 + (-40) = -39$
$2 \times (-20) = -40$	$2 + (-20) = -18$
$4 \times (-10) = -40$	$4 + (-10) = -6$
$5 \times (-8) = -40$	$5 + (-8) = -3$

The integers required are –5 and 8.

Step 2
Express $3x$ as $-5x + 8x$.
$$x^2 + 3x - 40$$
$$= x^2 - 5x + 8x - 40$$

Step 3
Group the terms, and remove the greatest common factor from each group.
$$x^2 - 5x + 8x - 40$$
$$= (x^2 - 5x) + (8x - 40)$$
$$= x(x - 5) + 8(x - 5)$$

Step 4
Factor out the common binomial.
$$x(x - 5) + 8(x - 5)$$
$$= (x - 5)(x + 8)$$

2. In $6x^2 - x - 15$, the product of the coefficient of x^2 and the constant term is $6 \times (-15) = -90$.
The middle term has a coefficient of -1.

Step 1
Find two integers that have a product of -90 and a sum of -1.

The pairs of integers with a product of -90 and their respective sums are as follows:

Product	Sum
$(-1) \times 90 = -90$	$(-1) + 90 = 89$
$(-2) \times 45 = -90$	$(-2) + 45 = 43$
$(-3) \times 30 = -90$	$(-3) + 30 = 27$
$(-5) \times 18 = -90$	$(-5) + 18 = 13$
$(-6) \times 15 = -90$	$(-6) + 15 = 9$
$(-9) \times 10 = -90$	$(-9) + 10 = 1$
$1 \times (-90) = -90$	$1 + (-90) = -89$
$2 \times (-45) = -90$	$2 + (-45) = -43$
$3 \times (-30) = -90$	$3 + (-30) = -27$
$5 \times (-18) = -90$	$5 + (-18) = -13$
$6 \times (-15) = -90$	$6 + (-15) = -9$
$\boxed{9 \times (-10) = -90}$	$\boxed{9 + (-10) = -1}$

The integers required are 9 and -10.

Step 2
Express $-x$ as $9x - 10x$.
$6x^2 - x - 15$
$= 6x^2 - 10x + 9x - 15$

Step 3
Group the terms, and remove the greatest common factor from each group.
$6x^2 - 10x + 9x - 15$
$= (6x^2 - 10x) + (9x - 15)$
$= 2x(3x - 5) + 3(3x - 5)$

Step 4
Factor out the common binomial.
$2x(3x - 5) + 3(3x - 5)$
$= (3x - 5)(2x + 3)$

3. **Step 1**
Factor out the greatest common factor from $9x^2 + 39x + 30$.

The greatest common factor is 3.
$9x^2 + 39x + 30$
$= 3(3x^2 + 13x + 10)$

In $3x^2 + 13 + 10$, the product of the coefficient of x^2 and the constant term is $3 \times 10 = 30$.
The middle term has a coefficient of 13.

Step 2
Find two integers that have a product of 30 and a sum of 13.

The pairs of integers with a product of 30 and their respective sums are as follows:

Product	Sum
$(-1) \times (-30) = 30$	$(-1) + (-30) = -31$
$(-2) \times (-15) = 30$	$(-2) + (-15) = -17$
$(-3) \times (-10) = 30$	$(-3) + (-10) = -13$
$(-5) \times (-6) = 30$	$(-6) + (-5) = -11$
$1 \times 30 = 30$	$1 + 30 = 31$
$2 \times 15 = 30$	$2 + 15 = 17$
$\boxed{3 \times 10 = 30}$	$\boxed{3 + 10 = 13}$
$5 \times 6 = 30$	$6 + 5 = 11$

The integers required are 3 and 10.

Step 3
Express $13x$ as $3x + 10x$.
$3(3x^2 + 13x + 10)$
$= 3(3x^2 + 3x + 10x + 10)$

Step 4
Group the terms, and remove the greatest common factor from each group.
$3(3x^2 + 3x + 10x + 10)$
$= 3[(3x^2 + 3x) + (10x + 10)]$
$= 3[3x(x + 1) + 10(x + 1)]$

Step 5
Factor out the common binomial.
$3[3x(x + 1) + 10(x + 1)]$
$= 3(x + 1)(3x + 10)$

4. In $-10x^2 - 19x - 6$, the product of the coefficient of x^2 and the constant term is $(-10) \times (-6) = 60$. The middle term has a coefficient of -19.

Step 1
Find two integers that have a product of 60 and a sum of -19.

The pairs of integers with a product of 60 and their respective sums are as follows:

Product	Sum
$(-1) \times (-60) = 60$	$(-1) + (-60) = -61$
$(-2) \times (-30) = 60$	$(-2) + (-30) = -32$
$(-3) \times (-20) = 60$	$(-3) + (-20) = -23$
$(-4) \times (-15) = 60$	$(-4) + (-15) = -19$
$(-5) \times (-12) = 60$	$(-5) + (-12) = -17$
$(-6) \times (-10) = 60$	$(-6) + (-10) = -16$
$1 \times 60 = 60$	$1 + 60 = 61$
$2 \times 30 = 60$	$2 + 30 = 32$
$3 \times 20 = 60$	$3 + 20 = 23$
$4 \times 15 = 60$	$4 + 15 = 19$
$5 \times 12 = 60$	$5 + 12 = 17$
$6 \times 10 = 60$	$6 + 10 = 16$

The integers required are -4 and -15.

Step 2
Express $-19x$ as $-4x - 15x$.
$-10x^2 - 19x - 6$
$= -10x^2 - 4x - 15x - 6$

Step 3
Group the terms, and remove the greatest common factor from each group.
$-10x^2 - 4x - 15x - 6$
$= (-10x^2 - 4x) + (-15x - 6)$
$= -2x(5x + 2) - 3(5x + 2)$

Step 4
Factor out the common binomial.
$-2x(5x + 2) - 3(5x + 2)$
$= (5x + 2)(-2x - 3)$
$= -(5x + 2)(2x + 3)$

Alternatively, -1 could have been factored out as a first step, $-\left(10x^2 + 19x + 6\right)$, followed by decomposition.

Factoring a Perfect Square Trinomial and a Difference of Squares

ANSWERS AND SOLUTIONS

1. Because the first and last terms are perfect squares, this trinomial may be a perfect square trinomial.

Step 1
Comparing the trinomial $64x^2 - 144x + 81$ to the form $a^2 - 2ab + b^2$, determine a and b.

$\begin{aligned} a^2 &= 64x^2 \\ a &= 8x \end{aligned}$ $\qquad \begin{aligned} b^2 &= 81 \\ b &= 9 \end{aligned}$

Since $2ab = 144x$, the trinomial $64x^2 - 144x + 81$ is a perfect square trinomial.

Step 2
Factor the trinomial.

The trinomial $64x^2 - 144x + 81$ is in the form $a^2 - 2ab + b^2$, which factors to $(a - b)^2$.
$64x^2 - 144x + 81$
$= (8x - 9)^2$

The trinomial $64x^2 - 144x + 81$ factors to $(8x - 9)(8x - 9)$, or $(8x - 9)^2$.

2. Because the first and last terms are perfect squares, this trinomial may be a perfect square trinomial.

Step 1
Comparing the trinomial $4m^2 + 20m + 25$ to the form $a^2 + 2ab + b^2$, determine a and b.

$\begin{aligned} a^2 &= 4m^2 \\ a &= 2m \end{aligned}$ $\qquad \begin{aligned} b^2 &= 25 \\ b &= 5 \end{aligned}$

Since $2ab = 20m$, the trinomial $4m^2 + 20m + 25$ is a perfect square trinomial.

Step 2
Factor the trinomial.

The trinomial $4m^2 + 20m + 25$ is in the form $a^2 + 2ab + b^2$, which factors to $(a + b)^2$.
$4m^2 + 20m + 25$
$= (2m + 5)^2$

The trinomial $4m^2 + 20m + 25$ factors to $(2m+5)(2m+5)$, or $(2m+5)^2$.

3. **Step 1**
Factor out the greatest common factor from each term of the trinomial. The greatest common factor of $-4n^2$, $4n$, and -1 is -1.
$-4n^2 + 4n - 1$
$= -(4n^2 - 4n + 1)$

Because the first and last terms of the trinomial are perfect squares, this trinomial may be a perfect square trinomial.

Step 2
Comparing the trinomial $4n^2 - 4n + 1$ to the form $a^2 - 2ab + b^2$, determine a and b.
$a^2 = 4n^2$ $\qquad b^2 = 1$
$a = 2n$ $\qquad\qquad b = 1$

Since $2ab = 4n$, the trinomial $4n^2 - 4n + 1$ is a perfect square trinomial.

Step 3
Factor the trinomial.

The trinomial $4n^2 - 4n + 1$ is in the form $a^2 - 2ab + b^2$, which factors to $(a-b)^2$.
$-(4n^2 - 4n + 1)$
$= -(2n-1)^2$

The trinomial $-4n^2 + 4n - 1$ factors to $-(2n-1)(2n-1)$, or $-(2n-1)^2$.

4. **Step 1**
Set up a product of two binomials, one with an addition operation and one with a subtraction operation.
$(\_ + \_)(\_ - \_)$

Step 2
Determine the square root of the first term in the difference-of-squares expression, and use the root as the first term in each of the bracketed binomials.
$\sqrt{x^2} = x \rightarrow (x + \_)(x - \_)$

Step 3
Determine the square root of the second term in the difference-of-squares expression, and use the root as the second term in each of the bracketed binomials.

$\sqrt{9y^2} = 3y \rightarrow (x+3y)(x-3y)$

Therefore, the factored form of the difference of squares $x^2 - 9y^2$ is $(x+3y)(x-3y)$.

5. **Step 1**
Set up a product of two binomials, one with an addition operation and one with a subtraction operation.
$(\_ + \_)(\_ - \_)$

Step 2
Determine the square root of the first term in the difference-of-squares expression, and use the root as the first term in each of the bracketed binomials.
$\sqrt{9m^2} = 3m \rightarrow (3m + \_)(3m - \_)$

Step 3
Determine the square root of the second term in the difference-of-squares expression, and use the root as the second term in each of the bracketed binomials.
$\sqrt{4n^2} = 2n \rightarrow (3m+2n)(3m-2n)$

Therefore, the factored form of the difference of squares $9m^2 - 4n^2$ is $(3m+2n)(3m-2n)$.

6. **Step 1**
Factor out the greatest common factor from each term of the binomial. The greatest common factor of -81 and $121y^2$ is -1.
$-81 + 121y^2$
$= -(81 - 121y^2)$

Step 2
Set up a product of two binomials, one with an addition operation and one with a subtraction operation.
$(\_ + \_)(\_ - \_)$

Step 3
Determine the square root of the first term in the difference-of-squares expression, and use the root as the first term in each of the bracketed binomials.
$\sqrt{81} = 9 \rightarrow (9 + \_)(9 - \_)$

Step 4
Determine the square root of the second term in the difference-of-squares expression, and use the root as the second term in each of the bracketed binomials.

$$\sqrt{121y^2} = 11y \rightarrow (9+11y)(9-11y)$$

Therefore, the factored form of the binomial $-81+121y^2$ is $-(9+11y)(9-11y)$.

Factoring Polynomial Expressions with Quadratic Patterns

ANSWERS AND SOLUTIONS

1. In $(x^2+1)^2 + (x^2+1) - 6$, the constant term is -6, and the middle term has a coefficient of 1.

Step 1
Find two integers with a product of -6 and a sum of 1.

The pairs of integers with a product of -6 and their respective sums are as follows:

Product	Sum
$(-1)\times 6 = -6$	$(-1)+6 = 5$
$\boxed{(-2)\times 3 = -6}$	$\boxed{(-2)+3 = 1}$
$(-3)\times 2 = -6$	$(-3)+2 = -1$
$1\times(-6) = -6$	$1+(-6) = -5$
$2\times(-3) = -6$	$2+(-3) = -1$
$3\times(-2) = -6$	$3+(-2) = 1$

The integers required are -2 and 3.

Step 2
Express (x^2+1) as $-2(x^2+1)+3(x^2+1)$.

$$(x^2+1)^2 + (x^2+1) - 6$$
$$= (x^2+1)^2 - 2(x^2+1) + 3(x^2+1) - 6$$

Step 3
Group the terms, and remove the greatest common factor from each group.

$$(x^2+1)^2 - 2(x^2+1) + 3(x^2+1) - 6$$
$$= [(x^2+1)^2 - 2(x^2+1)] + [3(x^2+1) - 6]$$
$$= (x^2+1)[(x^2+1) - 2] + 3[(x^2+1) - 2]$$

Step 4
Factor out the common binomial.

$$(x^2+1)[(x^2+1) - 2] + 3[(x^2+1) - 2]$$
$$= [(x^2+1) - 2][(x^2+1) + 3]$$

Step 5
Collect like terms in each binomial.

$$[(x^2+1) - 2][(x^2+1) + 3]$$
$$= (x^2-1)(x^2+4)$$

Step 6
Factor the difference of squares.

$$(x^2-1)(x^2+4)$$
$$= (x-1)(x+1)(x^2+4)$$

The trinomial $(x^2+1)^2 + (x^2+1) - 6$ factors to $(x-1)(x+1)(x^2+4)$.

2. In $2(x-9)^2 - 5(x-9) - 3$, the product of the coefficient of $(x^2-9)^2$ and the constant term is $2\times(-3) = -6$. The middle term has a coefficient of -5.

Step 1
Find two integers that have a product of -6 and a sum of -5.

The pairs of integers with a product of -6 and their respective sums are as follows:

Product	Sum
$(-1)\times 6 = -6$	$(-1)+6 = 5$
$(-2)\times 3 = -6$	$(-2)+3 = 1$
$(-3)\times 2 = -6$	$(-3)+2 = -1$
$\boxed{1\times(-6) = -6}$	$\boxed{1+(-6) = -5}$
$2\times(-3) = -6$	$2+(-3) = -1$
$3\times(-2) = -6$	$3+(-2) = 1$

The integers required are 1 and -6.

Step 2
Express $-5(x-9)$ as $(x-9)-6(x-9)$.

$$2(x-9)^2 - 5(x-9) - 3$$
$$= 2(x-9)^2 + (x-9) - 6(x-9) - 3$$

Step 3
Group the terms, and remove the greatest common factor from each group.
$$[2(x-9)^2+(x-9)]+[-6(x-9)-3]$$
$$=(x-9)[2(x-9)+1]-3[2(x-9)+1]$$

Step 4
Factor out the common binomial.
$$(x-9)[2(x-9)+1]-3[2(x-9)+1]$$
$$=[2(x-9)+1][(x-9)-3]$$

Step 5
Expand and collect like terms in each binomial.
$$[2(x-9)+1][(x-9)-3]$$
$$=(2x-18+1)(x-9-3)$$
$$=(2x-17)(x-12)$$

The trinomial $2(x-9)^2-5(x-9)-3$ factors to $(2x-17)(x-12)$.

3. **Step 1**
Set up a product of two binomials, one with an addition operation and one with a subtraction operation.
$$(\_+\_)(\_-\_)$$

Step 2
Determine the square root of the first term in the difference-of-squares expression, and use the root as the first term in each of the bracketed binomials.
$$\sqrt{4(x-7)^2}=2(x-7)$$
$$\rightarrow[2(x-7)+\_][2(x-7)-\_]$$

Step 3
Determine the square root of the second term in the difference-of-squares expression, and use the root as the second term in each of the bracketed binomials.
$$\sqrt{144(y+6)^2}=12(y+6)$$
$$\rightarrow[2(x-7)+12(y+6)][2(x-7)-12(y+6)]$$

Step 4
Expand and collect like terms in each binomial.
$$[2(x-7)+12(y+6)][2(x-7)-12(y+6)]$$
$$=(2x-14+12y+72)(2x-14-12y-72)$$
$$=(2x+12y+58)(2x-12y-86)$$

Therefore, the factored form of the difference of squares $4(x-7)^2-144(y+6)^2$ is $(2x+12y+58)(2x-12y-86)$.

4. **Step 1**
Set up a product of two binomials, one with an addition operation and one with a subtraction operation.
$$(\_+\_)(\_-\_)$$

Step 2
Determine the square root of the first term in the difference-of-squares expression, and use the root as the first term in each of the bracketed binomials.
$$\sqrt{16x^2}=4x\rightarrow[4x+\_][4x-\_]$$

Step 3
Determine the square root of the second term in the difference-of-squares expression, and use the root as the second term in each of the bracketed binomials.
$$\sqrt{49(y-3)^2}=7(y-3)$$
$$\rightarrow[4x+7(y-3)][4x-7(y-3)]$$

Step 4
Expand and collect like terms in each binomial.
$$[4x+7(y-3)][4x-7(y-3)]$$
$$=(4x+7y-21)(4x-7y+21)$$

Therefore, the factored form of the difference of squares $16x^2-49(y-3)^2$ is $(4x+7y-21)(4x-7y+21)$.

ANSWERS AND SOLUTIONS

1. In $x^2 - 4x - 21$, the constant term is –21, and the middle term has a coefficient of –4.

Step 1
Find two integers with a product of –21 and a sum of –4.

The pairs of integers with a product of –21 and their respective sums are as follows:

Product	Sum
$(-1) \times 21 = -21$	$(-1) + 21 = 20$
$(-3) \times 7 = -21$	$(-3) + 7 = 4$
$1 \times (-21) = -21$	$1 + (-21) = -20$
$\boxed{3 \times (-7) = -21}$	$\boxed{3 + (-7) = -4}$

The integers required are 3 and –7.
Step 2
Express $-4x$ as $3x - 7x$.
$x^2 - 4x - 21$
$= x^2 + 3x - 7x - 21$

Step 3
Group the terms, and remove the greatest common factor from each group.
$x^2 + 3x - 7x - 21$
$= (x^2 + 3x) + (-7x - 21)$
$= x(x + 3) - 7(x + 3)$

Step 4
Factor out the common binomial.
$x(x + 3) - 7(x + 3)$
$= (x + 3)(x - 7)$

2. In $2x^2 + 13x + 15$, the product of the coefficient of x^2 and the constant term is $2 \times 15 = 30$.
The middle term has a coefficient of 13.

Step 1
Find two integers that have a product of 30 and a sum of 13.

The pairs of integers with a product of 30 and their respective sums are as follows:

Product	Sum
$(-1) \times (-30) = 30$	$(-1) + (-30) = -31$
$(-2) \times (-15) = 30$	$(-2) + (-15) = -17$
$(-3) \times (-10) = 30$	$(-3) + (-10) = -13$
$(-5) \times (-6) = 30$	$(-5) + (-6) = -11$
$1 \times 30 = 30$	$1 + 30 = 31$
$2 \times 15 = 30$	$2 + 15 = 17$
$\boxed{3 \times 10 = 30}$	$\boxed{3 + 10 = 13}$
$5 \times 6 = 30$	$5 + 6 = 11$

The integers required are 3 and 10.

Step 2
Express $13x$ as $3x + 10x$.
$2x^2 + 13x + 15$
$= 2x^2 + 3x + 10x + 15$

Step 3
Group the terms, and remove the greatest common factor from each group.
$2x^2 + 3x + 10x + 15$
$= (2x^2 + 3x) + (10x + 15)$
$= x(2x + 3) + 5(2x + 3)$
Step 4
Factor out the common binomial.
$x(2x + 3) + 5(2x + 3)$
$= (2x + 3)(x + 5)$

3. Because the first and last terms are perfect squares, this trinomial may be a perfect square trinomial.

Step 1
Comparing the trinomial $225x^2 - 30x + 1$ to the form $a^2 - 2ab + b^2$, determine a and b.
$a^2 = 225x^2 \qquad b^2 = 1$
$a = 15x \qquad b = 1$

Since $2ab = 30x$, the trinomial $225x^2 - 30x + 1$ is a perfect square trinomial.

Step 2
Factor the trinomial.

The trinomial $225x^2 - 30x + 1$ is in the form $a^2 - 2ab + b^2$, which factors to $(a - b)^2$.
$225x^2 - 30x + 1$
$= (15x - 1)^2$

The trinomial $225x^2 - 30x + 1$ factors to $(15x - 1)(15x - 1)$, or $(15x - 1)^2$.

4. **Step 1**
Factor out the greatest common factor from each term of the trinomial. The greatest common factor of $24x^2$, $120x$, and 150 is 6.

$24x^2 + 120x + 150$
$= 6(4x^2 + 20x + 25)$

Because the first and last terms of the trinomial are perfect squares, this trinomial may be a perfect square trinomial.

Step 2
Comparing the trinomial $4x^2 + 20x + 25$ to the form $a^2 + 2ab + b^2$, determine a and b.

$a^2 = 4x^2 \qquad\qquad b^2 = 25$
$\quad a = 2x \qquad\qquad\quad b = 5$

Since $2ab = 20x$, the trinomial $4x^2 + 20x + 25$ is a perfect square trinomial.

Step 3
Factor the trinomial.

The trinomial $4x^2 + 20x + 25$ is in the form $a^2 + 2ab + b^2$, which factors to $(a+b)^2$.

$6(4x^2 + 20x + 25)$
$= 6(2x+5)^2$

The trinomial $24x^2 + 120x + 150$ factors to $6(2x+5)(2x+5)$, or $6(2x+5)^2$.

5. **Step 1**
Set up a product of two binomials, one with an addition operation and one with a subtraction operation.
$(\underline{} + \underline{})(\underline{} - \underline{})$

Step 2
Determine the square root of the first term in the difference-of-squares expression, and use the root as the first term in each of the bracketed binomials.
$\sqrt{36x^2} = 6x \rightarrow (6x + \underline{})(6x - \underline{})$

Step 3
Determine the square root of the second term in the difference-of-squares expression, and use the root as the second term in each of the bracketed binomials.
$\sqrt{49y^2} = 7y \rightarrow (6x + 7y)(6x - 7y)$
Therefore, the factored form of the difference of squares $36x^2 - 49y^2$ is $(6x+7y)(6x-7y)$.

6. **Step 1**
Factor out the greatest common factor from each term of the binomial. The greatest common factor of $45x^2$ and $125y^2$ is 5.

$45x^2 - 125y^2$
$= 5(9x^2 - 25y^2)$

Step 2
Set up a product of two binomials, one with an addition operation and one with a subtraction operation.
$(\underline{} + \underline{})(\underline{} - \underline{})$

Step 3
Determine the square root of the first term in the difference-of-squares expression, and use the root as the first term in each of the bracketed binomials.
$\sqrt{9x^2} = 3x \rightarrow (3x + \underline{})(3x - \underline{})$

Step 4
Determine the square root of the second term in the difference-of-squares expression, and use the root as the second term in each of the bracketed binomials.
$\sqrt{25y^2} = 5y \rightarrow (3x + 5y)(3x - 5y)$

Therefore, the factored form of the binomial $45x^2 - 125y^2$ is $5(3x+5y)(3x-5y)$.

7. In $(x+6)^2 - 8(x+6) + 15$, the constant term is 15, and the middle term has a coefficient of -8.

Step 1
Find two integers with a product of 15 and a sum of -8.

The pairs of integers with a product of 15 and their respective sums are as follows:

Product	Sum
$(-1) \times (-15) = 15$	$(-1) + (-15) = -16$
$(-3) \times (-5) = 15$	$(-3) + (-5) = -8$
$1 \times 15 = 15$	$1 + 15 = 16$
$3 \times 5 = 15$	$3 + 5 = 8$

The integers required are -3 and -5.

Step 2
Express $-8(x+6)$ as $-3(x+6)-5(x+6)$.
$(x+6)^2 - 8(x+6) + 15$
$= (x+6)^2 - 3(x+6) - 5(x+6) + 15$

Step 3
Group the terms, and remove the greatest common factor from each group.
$(x+6)^2 - 3(x+6) - 5(x+6) + 15$
$= [(x+6)^2 - 3(x+6)] + [-5(x+6) + 15]$
$= (x+6)[(x+6) - 3] - 5[(x+6) - 3]$

Step 4
Factor out the common binomial.
$(x+6)[(x+6)-3] - 5[(x+6)-3]$
$= [(x+6)-3][(x+6)-5]$

Step 5
Collect like terms in each binomial.
$[(x+6)-3][(x+6)-5]$
$= (x+3)(x+1)$

The trinomial $(x+6)^2 - 8(x+6) + 15$ factors to $(x+3)(x+1)$.

8. **Step 1**
Set up a product of two binomials, one with an addition operation and one with a subtraction operation.
$(\_ + \_)(\_ - \_)$

Step 2
Determine the square root of the first term in the difference-of-squares expression, and use the root as the first term in each of the bracketed binomials.
$\sqrt{81(x-7)^2} = 9(x-7)$
$\rightarrow [9(x-7) + \_\_][9(x-7) - \_\_]$

Step 3
Determine the square root of the second term in the difference-of-squares expression, and use the root as the second term in each of the bracketed binomials.
$\sqrt{16y^2} = 4y$
$\rightarrow [9(x-7) + 4y][9(x-7) - 4y]$

Step 4
Expand and collect like terms in each binomial.
$[9(x-7) + 4y][9(x-7) - 4y]$
$= (9x - 63 + 4y)(9x - 63 - 4y)$
$= (9x + 4y - 63)(9x - 4y - 63)$

Therefore, the factored form of the difference of squares $81(x-7)^2 - 16y^2$ is $(9x + 4y - 63)(9x - 4y - 63)$.

ABSOLUTE VALUE FUNCTIONS

The Absolute Value of Real Numbers

PRACTICE EXERCISES
ANSWERS AND SOLUTIONS

1. **Step 1**
Perform the operation inside the absolute value.
$|24 - 9| = |15|$

The expression simplifies to .

Step 2
Replace the absolute value with its equivalent positive number.
$|15| = 15$

2. **Step 1**
Perform the operation inside the absolute value.

The expression simplifies to $|-2|$.

Step 2
Replace the absolute value with its equivalent positive number.
$|-2| = 2$

3. **Step 1**
Replace each absolute value with its equivalent positive number.
$|-7.2| + |16.3|$
$= (7.2) + (16.3)$

Step 2
Perform the calculation.
$(7.2) + (16.3)$
$= 23.5$

The value of the expression $|-7.2| + |16.3|$ is 23.5.

4. **Step 1**
Replace each absolute value with its equivalent positive number.
$|-9| \times |6| \div |-3|$
$= (9) \times (6) \div (3)$

Step 2
Perform the calculations following proper order of operations.
$(9) \times (6) \div (3)$
$= 9 \times 2$
$= 18$

The value of the expression $|-9| \times |6| \div |-3|$ is 18.

5. **Step 1**
Perform the operation inside the first absolute value.
The expression now simplifies to $|-5| + |9| \times |-5|$.

Step 2 $\dfrac{|-4| - |10| \div |-5|}{= (4) - (10) \div (5)}$
Replace each absolute value with its equivalent positive number.
$|-5| + |9| \times |-5|$
$= (5) + (9) \times (5)$

Step 3
Perform the calculations following proper order of operations.
$(5) + (9) \times (5)$
$= 5 + 45$
$= 50$

The value of the expression $|-8 + 3| + |9| \times |-5|$ is 50.

6. **Step 1**
Perform the operation inside the second absolute value.
$|12 - 2| = |10|$

The expression now simplifies to $|-4| - |10| \div |-5|$.

Step 2
Replace each absolute value with its equivalent positive number.

Step 3
Perform the calculations following proper order of operations.
$(4) - (10) \div (5)$
$= 4 - 2$
$= 2$
The value of the expression $|-4| - |12 - 2| \div |-5|$ is 2.

7. **Step 1**
Perform all operations inside the absolute values.
$|-36 \div 2 - 10|$
$= |-18 - 10|$
$= |-28|$

$|-7 \times -2|$
$= |14|$

The expression simplifies to $|-28| \div |14| - |9|$.

Step 2
Replace each absolute value with its equivalent positive value.
$(28) \div (14) - (9)$

Step 3
Evaluate the expression following proper order of operations.
$(28) \div (14) - (9)$
$= 2 - 9$
$= -7$

The value of $|-36 \div 2 - 10| \div |-7 \times -2| - |9|$ is -7.

8. **Step 1**
Perform all operations inside the absolute values.
$|100 \div 5| = |20| \qquad |-16 - 8| = |-24|$

The expression simplifies to $|20| \div |-4| + |-24| + |7|$.

Step 2
Replace each absolute value with its equivalent positive value.
$(20) \div (4) + (24) + (7)$

Step 3
Evaluate the expression following proper order of operations.
$(20) \div (4) + (24) + (7)$
$= 5 + 24 + 7$
$= 29 + 7$
$= 36$

The value of $|100 \div 5| \div |-4| + |-16 - 8| + |7|$ is 36.

Analyzing Absolute Value Functions

ANSWERS AND SOLUTIONS

1. **Step 1**
Apply the definition of an absolute value.

If $(x+3) \geq 0$, which means $x \geq -3$,
then $|x+3| = x+3$.
If $(x+3) < 0$, which means $x < -3$,
then $|x+3| = -(x+3)$.

Step 2
Express $y = |x+3|$ as a piecewise function.
$$y = \begin{cases} x+3, & x \geq -3 \\ -(x+3), & x < -3 \end{cases}$$

Step 3
Construct a table of values for the piecewise function.

$y = x+3, x \geq -3$		$y = -(x+3), x < -3$	
x	y	x	y
−3	0		
−2	1	−4	1
−1	2	−5	2
0	3	−6	3
1	4	−7	4

Step 4
Sketch the graph.

Plot the ordered pairs from the table of values on a Cartesian plane, and draw lines through the points to give a graph of the function.

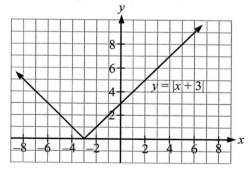

Step 5
State the intercepts and the domain and range.

The graph of $y = |x+3|$ intersects the x-axis at $(-3, 0)$ and the y-axis at $(0, 3)$.

The domain is $x \in \mathbb{R}$, and the range is $y \geq 0$.

2. **Step 1**
Apply the definition of an absolute value.

If $(x-7) \geq 0$, which means $x \geq 7$,
then $|x-7| = x-7$.
If $(x-7) < 0$, which means $x < 7$,
then $|x-7| = -(x-7)$.

Step 2
Express $y = |x-7|$ as a piecewise function.
$$y = \begin{cases} x-7, & x \geq 7 \\ -(x-7), & x < 7 \end{cases}$$

Step 3
Construct a table of values for the piecewise function.

$y = x-7, x \geq 7$		$y = -(x-7), x < 7$	
x	y	x	y
7	0		
8	1	6	1
9	2	5	2
10	3	4	3
11	4	3	4

Step 4
Sketch the graph.
Plot the ordered pairs from the table of values on a Cartesian plane, and draw lines through the points to give a graph of the function.

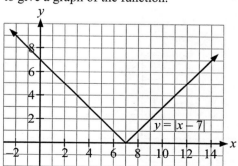

Step 5
State the intercepts and the domain and range.

The graph of $y = |x - 7|$ intersects the x-axis at $(7, 0)$ and the y-axis at $(7, 0)$.

The domain is $x \in \mathrm{R}$, and the range is $y \geq 0$.

3. **Step 1**
Apply the definition of an absolute value.

If $(-x - 4) \geq 0$, which means $x \leq -4$,
then $|-x - 4| = (-x - 4)$.
If $(-x - 4) < 0$, which means $x > -4$,
then $|-x - 4| = -(-x - 4)$.

Step 2
Express $y = |-x - 4|$ as a piecewise function.

$$y = \begin{cases} -x - 4, & x \leq -4 \\ x + 4, & x > -4 \end{cases}$$

Step 3
Construct a table of values for the piecewise function.

$y = -x - 4, x \leq -4$		$y = x + 4, x > -4$	
x	y	x	y
-4	0		
-5	1	-3	1
-6	2	-2	2
-7	3	-1	3
-8	4	0	4

Step 4
Sketch the graph.

Plot the ordered pairs from the table of values on a Cartesian plane, and draw lines through the points to give a graph of the function.

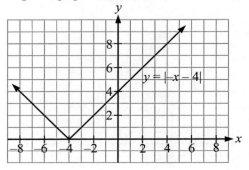

Step 5
State the intercepts and the domain and range.

The graph of $y = |-x - 4|$ intersects the x-axis at $(-4, 0)$ and the y-axis at $(0, 4)$.

The domain is $x \in \mathrm{R}$, and the range is $y \geq 0$.

4. **Step 1**
Let $f(x) = x^2 - 6$.

Sketch the graph of $f(x) = x^2 - 6$.

The graph of $f(x) = x^2 - 6$ can be sketched by transforming the graph of the parabola $y = x^2$ 6 units down or by using a TI-83 or similar graphing calculator.

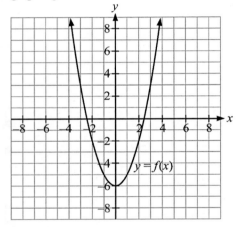

Step 2
Identify points where the graph of $y = f(x)$ is zero or positive (above the x-axis) and where the graph of $y = f(x)$ is negative (below the x-axis).

Using a TI-83 or similar graphing calculator, press 2nd TRACE, and select 2:zero to determine that the function $f(x)$ is zero or positive when $x \leq -2.4$ and $x \geq 2.4$. The function is negative when $-2.4 < x < 2.4$.

Step 3
Reflect the negative parts of $y = f(x)$ about the x-axis.

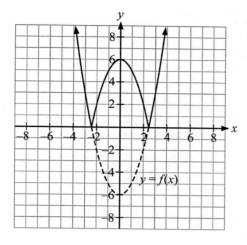

Step 4

Show the sketch of $y = |f(x)|$.

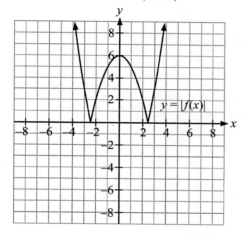

Step 5

State the intercepts and the domain and range of the function.

The graph of $y = |x^2 - 6|$ intersects the x-axis at $(-2.4, 0)$ and $(2.4, 0)$. The y-intercept is $(0, 6)$.

The domain is $x \in \mathbb{R}$. The range of the function $y = |f(x)|$ is $y \geq 0$.

5. Step 1

Let $f(x) = x^2 + 6x - 5$.

Sketch the graph of $f(x) = x^2 + 6x - 5$.

The graph of $f(x) = x^2 + 6x - 5$ can be sketched by completing the square, $f(x) = (x+3)^2 - 14$, and plotting known points (such as the vertex and intercepts) or using a TI-83 or similar graphing calculator.

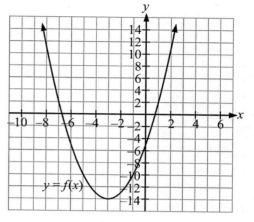

Step 2

Identify points where the graph of $y = f(x)$ is zero or positive (above the x-axis) and where the graph of $y = f(x)$ is negative (below the x-axis).

Using a TI-83 or similar graphing calculator, press $\boxed{\text{2nd}}$ $\boxed{\text{TRACE}}$, and select 2:zero to determine that the function $f(x)$ is zero or positive when $x \leq -6.7$ and $x \geq 0.7$. The function is negative when $-6.7 < x < 0.7$.

Step 3

Reflect the negative parts of $y = f(x)$ about the x-axis.

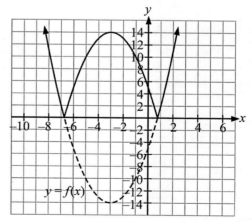

Step 4
Show the sketch of $y = |f(x)|$.

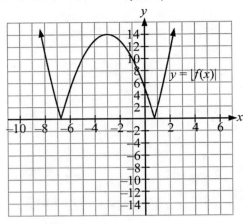

Step 5
State the intercepts and the domain and range of the function.

The graph of $y = |x^2 + 6x - 5|$ intersects the x-axis at $(-6.7, 0)$ and $(0.7, 0)$. The y-intercept is $(0, 5)$.

The domain is $x \in \mathbb{R}$, and the range of the function $y = |f(x)|$ is $y \geq 0$.

6. Step 1
Let $f(x) = -x^2 + 3x + 1$.

Sketch the graph of $f(x) = -x^2 + 3x + 1$.

The graph of $f(x) = -x^2 + 3x + 1$ can be sketched by completing the square, $f(x) = -\left(x - \dfrac{3}{2}\right)^2 + \dfrac{13}{4}$, and plotting known points (such as the vertex and intercepts) or using a TI-83 or similar graphing calculator.

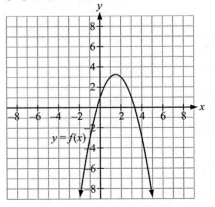

Step 2
Identify points where the graph of $y = f(x)$ is zero or positive (above the x-axis) and where the graph of $y = f(x)$ is negative (below the x-axis).

Using a TI-83 or similar graphing calculator, press 2nd TRACE, and select 2:zero to determine that the function $f(x)$ is zero or positive when $-0.3 \leq x \leq 3.3$. The function is negative when $x < -0.3$ and $x > 3.3$.

Step 3
Reflect the negative parts of $y = f(x)$ about the x-axis.

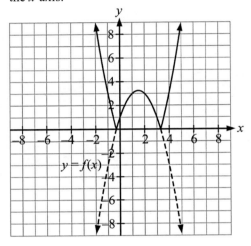

Step 4
Show the sketch of $y = |f(x)|$.

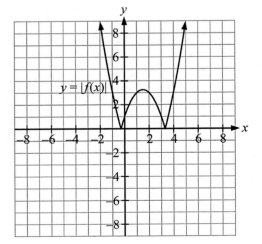

Step 5
State the intercepts and the domain and range of the function.

The graph of $y=\left|-x^2+3x+1\right|$ intersects the x-axis at $(-0.3, 0)$ and $(3.3, 0)$. The y-intercept is $(0, 1)$.

The domain is $x \in \mathbb{R}$, and the range of the function $y=\left|f(x)\right|$ is $y \geq 0$.

Solving Absolute Value Equations

ANSWERS AND SOLUTIONS

1. **Step 1**
   Multiply both sides of the equation by -1.
   $$-3 = -\left|3x-1\right|$$
   $$3 = \left|3x-1\right|$$

   Step 2
   Apply the definition of absolute value.

   If $3x-1 \geq 0$, which means $x \geq \dfrac{1}{3}$,
   then $\left|3x-1\right| = 3x-1$.

   If $3x-1 < 0$, which means $x < \dfrac{1}{3}$,
   then $\left|3x-1\right| = -(3x-1)$.

   The outcome is two equations that are solved separately.

   Step 3
   Solve for x if $3x-1 \geq 0$.
   $$3 = \left|3x-1\right|$$
   $$3 = 3x-1$$
   $$4 = 3x$$
   $$\frac{4}{3} = x$$

   Step 4
   Solve for x if $3x-1 < 0$.
   $$3 = \left|3x-1\right|$$
   $$3 = -(3x-1)$$
   $$3 = -3x+1$$
   $$3x = -2$$
   $$x = -\frac{2}{3}$$

Step 5
Verify the solutions.

Both values appear to be valid because $x = \dfrac{4}{3}$ satisfies $x \geq \dfrac{1}{3}$ and $x = -\dfrac{2}{3}$ satisfies $x < \dfrac{1}{3}$.

Substitute these solutions into the original equation to verify.

$x = \dfrac{4}{3}$		$x = -\dfrac{2}{3}$	
LHS	**RHS**	**LHS**	**RHS**
-3	$-\left|3\left(\dfrac{4}{3}\right)-1\right|$	-3	$-\left|3\left(-\dfrac{2}{3}\right)-1\right|$
	$-\left|4-1\right|$		$-\left|-2-1\right|$
	$-\left|3\right|$		$-\left|-3\right|$
	-3		-3

The solution set is $\left\{-\dfrac{2}{3}, \dfrac{4}{3}\right\}$.

2. **Step 1**
   Apply the definition of absolute value.

   If $(3x-4) \geq 0$, which means $x \geq \dfrac{4}{3}$,
   then $\left|3x-4\right| = 3x-4$.

   If $(3x-4) < 0$, which means $x < \dfrac{4}{3}$,
   then $\left|3x-4\right| = -(3x-4)$.

   The outcome is two equations that are solved separately.

   Step 2
   Solve for x if $(3x-4) \geq 0$.
   $$\left|3x-4\right| = 2x+1$$
   $$3x-4 = 2x+1$$
   $$x = 5$$

   Step 3
   Solve for x if $(3x-4) < 0$.

$$|3x-4| = 2x+1$$
$$-(3x-4) = 2x+1$$
$$-3x+4 = 2x+1$$
$$-5x = -3$$
$$x = \frac{3}{5}$$

Step 4
Verify the solutions.

Both values appear to be valid because $x = 5$ satisfies $x \geq \frac{4}{3}$ and $x = \frac{3}{5}$ satisfies $x < \frac{4}{3}$.

Substitute these solutions into the original equation to verify.

$x = \dfrac{3}{5}$		$x = 5$	
LHS	**RHS**	**LHS**	**RHS**
$\left\|3\left(\dfrac{3}{5}\right)-4\right\|$ $\left\|\dfrac{9}{5}-\dfrac{20}{5}\right\|$ $\left\|-\dfrac{11}{5}\right\|$ $\dfrac{11}{5}$	$2\left(\dfrac{3}{5}\right)+1$ $\dfrac{6}{5}+\dfrac{5}{5}$ $\dfrac{11}{5}$	$\|3(5)-4\|$ $\|15-4\|$ $\|11\|$ 11	$2(5)+1$ $10+1$ 11

The solution set is $\left\{\dfrac{3}{5}, 5\right\}$.

3. **Step 1**
Apply the definition of absolute value.

If $(3x+4) \geq 0$, which means $x \geq -\dfrac{4}{3}$, then $|3x+4| = 3x+4$.

If $(3x+4) < 0$, which means $x < -\dfrac{4}{3}$, then $|3x+4| = -(3x+4)$.

The outcome is two equations that are solved separately.

Step 2
Solve for x if $(3x+4) \geq 0$.

$$|3x+4| = 13$$
$$3x+4 = 13$$
$$3x = 9$$
$$x = 3$$

Step 3
Solve for x if $(3x+4) < 0$.

Step 4
Verify the solutions.

Both values appear to be valid because $x = 3$ satisfies $x \geq -\dfrac{4}{3}$ and $x = -\dfrac{17}{3}$ satisfies $x < -\dfrac{4}{3}$.

Substitute these solutions into the original equation to verify.

$x = 3$		$x = -\dfrac{17}{3}$	
LHS	**RHS**	**LHS**	**RHS**
$\|3(3)+4\|$ $\|9+4\|$ $\|13\|$ 13	13	$\left\|3\left(-\dfrac{17}{3}\right)+4\right\|$ $\|-17+4\|$ $\|-13\|$ 13	13

The solution set is $\left\{-\dfrac{17}{3}, 3\right\}$.

4. **Step 1**
Apply the definition of absolute value.

If $(x^2+6x+5) \geq 0$, then $|x^2+6x+5| = x^2+6x+5$.

If $(x^2+6x+5) < 0$, then .

The outcome is two equations that are solved separately.

Step 2
Solve for x if $(x^2+6x+5) \geq 0$.

$$|x^2+6x+5| = x+1$$
$$x^2+6x+5 = x+1$$
$$x^2+5x+4 = 0$$
$$x^2+x+4x+4 = 0$$
$$x(x+1)+4(x+1) = 0$$
$$(x+4)(x+1) = 0$$
$$x+4 = 0 \quad \text{or} \quad x+1 = 0$$
$$x = -4 \qquad\qquad x = -1$$

Step 3

Solve for x if $\left(x^2 + 6x + 5\right) < 0$.

$$\left|x^2 + 6x + 5\right| = x + 1$$
$$-\left(x^2 + 6x + 5\right) = x + 1$$
$$-x^2 - 6x - 5 = x + 1$$
$$-x^2 - 7x - 6 = 0$$
$$x^2 + 7x + 6 = 0$$
$$x^2 + x + 6x + 6 = 0$$
$$x(x+1) + 6(x+1) = 0$$
$$(x+6)(x+1) = 0$$
$$x + 6 = 0 \quad \text{or} \quad x + 1 = 0$$
$$x = -6 \qquad\qquad x = -1$$

Step 4

Verify the solutions.

The possible solutions are $x = -6$, $x = -4$, and $x = -1$.

Substitute these solutions into the original equation and verify.

$x = -6$	
LHS	**RHS**
$\left\|(-6)^2 + 6(-6) + 5\right\|$	$(-6) + 1$
$\left\|36 - 36 + 5\right\|$	$-6 + 1$
$\left\|5\right\|$	-5
5	

The LHS $\neq$ RHS, so $x = -6$ is an extraneous solution.

$x = -4$	
LHS	**RHS**
$\left\|(-4)^2 + 6(-4) + 5\right\|$	$(-4) + 1$
$\left\|16 - 24 + 5\right\|$	$-4 + 1$
$\left\|-3\right\|$	-3
3	

The LHS $\neq$ RHS, so $x = -4$ is an extraneous solution.

$x = -1$	
LHS	**RHS**
$\left\|(-1)^2 + 6(-1) + 5\right\|$	$(-1) + 1$
$\left\|1 - 6 + 5\right\|$	$-1 + 1$
$\left\|0\right\|$	0
0	

The LHS $=$ RHS, so $x = -1$ is a valid solution.

The solution set is $\{-1\}$.

5. **Step 1**

Apply the definition of absolute value.

If $\left(2x^2 + x - 6\right) \geq 0$, then

$$\left|2x^2 + x - 6\right| = 2x^2 + x - 6.$$

If $\left(2x^2 + x - 6\right) < 0$, then

$$\left|2x^2 + x - 6\right| = -\left(2x^2 + x - 6\right).$$

The outcome is two equations that are solved separately.

Step 2

Solve for x if $\left(2x^2 + x - 6\right) \geq 0$.

$$\left|2x^2 + x - 6\right| = 4x + 3$$
$$2x^2 + x - 6 = 4x + 3$$
$$2x^2 - 3x - 9 = 0$$
$$2x^2 - 6x + 3x - 9 = 0$$
$$2x(x-3) + 3(x-3) = 0$$
$$(2x+3)(x-3) = 0$$
$$2x + 3 = 0 \quad \text{or} \quad x - 3 = 0$$
$$x = -\frac{3}{2} \qquad\qquad x = 3$$

Step 3

Solve for x if $\left(2x^2 + x - 6\right) < 0$.

$$\left|2x^2 + x - 6\right| = 4x + 3$$
$$-\left(2x^2 + x - 6\right) = 4x + 3$$
$$-2x^2 - x + 6 = 4x + 3$$
$$-2x^2 - 5x + 3 = 0$$
$$2x^2 + 5x - 3 = 0$$
$$2x^2 + 6x - x - 3 = 0$$
$$2x(x+3) - 1(x+3) = 0$$
$$(2x-1)(x+3) = 0$$
$$2x - 1 = 0 \quad \text{or} \quad x + 3 = 0$$
$$x = \frac{1}{2} \qquad\qquad x = -3$$

Step 4
Verify the solutions.

The possible solutions are $x = -3$, $x = -\dfrac{3}{2}$, $x = \dfrac{1}{2}$, and $x = 3$.

Substitute these solutions into the original equation and verify.

$x = -3$	
LHS	**RHS**
$\left\|2(-3)^2 + (-3) - 6\right\|$ $\left\|2(9) - 3 - 6\right\|$ $\left\|18 - 9\right\|$ $\left\|9\right\|$ 9	$4(-3) + 3$ $-12 + 3$ -9

The $\text{LHS} \neq \text{RHS}$, so $x = -3$ is an extraneous solution.

$x = -\dfrac{3}{2}$	
LHS	**RHS**
$\left\|2\left(-\dfrac{3}{2}\right)^2 + \left(-\dfrac{3}{2}\right) - 6\right\|$ $\left\|2\left(\dfrac{9}{4}\right) - \dfrac{3}{2} - 6\right\|$ $\left\|\dfrac{9}{2} - \dfrac{3}{2} - 6\right\|$ $\left\|\dfrac{6}{2} - 6\right\|$ $\left\|3 - 6\right\|$ $\left\|-3\right\|$ 3	$4\left(-\dfrac{3}{2}\right) + 3$ $-6 + 3$ -3

The $\text{LHS} \neq \text{RHS}$, so $x = -\dfrac{3}{2}$ is an extraneous solution.

$x = \dfrac{1}{2}$	
LHS	**RHS**
$\left\|2\left(\dfrac{1}{2}\right)^2 + \left(\dfrac{1}{2}\right) - 6\right\|$ $\left\|2\left(\dfrac{1}{4}\right) + \dfrac{1}{2} - 6\right\|$ $\left\|\dfrac{1}{2} + \dfrac{1}{2} - 6\right\|$ $\left\|-5\right\|$ 5	$4\left(\dfrac{1}{2}\right) + 3$ $2 + 3$ 5

The $\text{LHS} = \text{RHS}$, so $x = \dfrac{1}{2}$ is a valid solution.

$x = 3$	
LHS	**RHS**
$\left\|2(3)^2 + (3) - 6\right\|$ $\left\|2(9) + 3 - 6\right\|$ $\left\|18 - 3\right\|$ $\left\|15\right\|$ 15	$4(3) + 3$ $12 + 3$ 15

The $\text{LHS} = \text{RHS}$, so $x = 3$ is a valid solution.

The solution set is $\left\{\dfrac{1}{2}, 3\right\}$.

6. **Step 1**
    Break the equation into two separate functions.

    Write the left side of the equation as Y_1 and the right side as Y_2.
    $Y_1 = |4x - 5| - x$ and $Y_2 = 19$.

    Step 2
    Graph the two functions using a TI-83 or similar graphing calculator.

    Press $\boxed{Y =}$, and input the functions $Y_1 = |4x - 5| - x$ and $Y_2 = 19$ as shown in the given window.

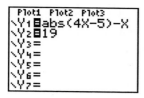

Use the window settings of $x:[-5,10,1]$ and $y:[-5,40,1]$, and then press $\boxed{\text{GRAPH}}$ to obtain this window.

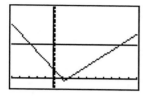

Step 3
Determine the points of intersection of the two graphs.

Press $\boxed{\text{2nd}}$ $\boxed{\text{TRACE}}$, and select 5:intersect to determine the points of intersection.

The x-coordinates of the points of intersection are $x = -2.8$ and $x = 8$.

The solution set is $\{-2.8, 8\}$.

7. Step 1
Break the equation into two separate functions.

Write the left side of the equation as Y_1 and the right side as Y_2.
$Y_1 = |x+3|$ and $Y_2 = |x-1|+6$.

Step 2
Graph the two functions using a TI-83 or similar graphing calculator.

Press $\boxed{Y=}$, and input the functions $Y_1 = |x+3|$ and $Y_2 = |x-1|+6$ as shown in the given window.

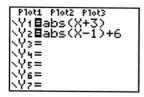

Use the window settings of $x:[-10,10,1]$ and $y:[-10,10,1]$ then press $\boxed{\text{GRAPH}}$ to obtain this window.

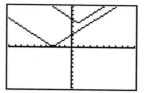

Step 3
Determine the points of intersection of the two graphs.

Since there are no intersection points for the graphs, there is no solution to the equation $|x+3| = |x-1|+6$.

8. Step 1
Break the equation into two separate functions.

Write the left side of the equation as Y_1 and the right side as Y_2.
$Y_1 = |1-2x|$ and $Y_2 = 12x-7$.

Step 2
Graph the two functions using a TI-83 or similar graphing calculator.

Press $\boxed{Y=}$, and input the functions $Y_1 = |1-2x|$ and $Y_2 = 12x-7$ as shown in the given window.

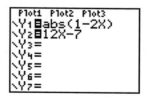

Use the window settings of $x:[-5,5,1]$ and $y:[-5,5,1]$, and then press $\boxed{\text{GRAPH}}$ to obtain this window.

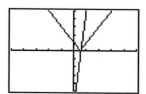

125

Step 3
Determine the points of intersection of the two graphs.

Press $\boxed{\text{2nd}}$ $\boxed{\text{TRACE}}$, and select 5:intersect to determine the points of intersection. At the point of intersection, the x-coordinate is $x = 0.6$.

The solution set is $\{0.6\}$.

9. **Step 1**
Break the equation into two separate functions.

Write the left side of the equation as Y_1 and the right side as Y_2.
$Y_1 = |x| + |3 - x|$ and $Y_2 = 12$.

Step 2
Graph the two functions using a TI-83 or similar graphing calculator.

Press $\boxed{Y =}$, and input the functions $Y_1 = |x| + |3 - x|$ and $Y_2 = 12$ as shown in the given window.

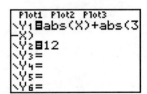

Use the window settings of $x:[-10,10,1]$ and $y:[-10,15,1]$, and then press $\boxed{\text{GRAPH}}$ to obtain this window.

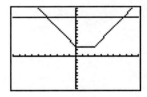

Step 3
Determine the points of intersection of the two graphs.

Press $\boxed{\text{2nd}}$ $\boxed{\text{TRACE}}$, and select 5:intersect to determine the points of intersection. At the points of intersection, the x-coordinates are $x = -4.5$ and $x = 7.5$.

The solution set is $\{-4.5, 7.5\}$.

10. **Step 1**
Break the equation into two separate functions.
$Y_1 = |x^2 + x - 6| + |x|$ and $Y_2 = 4$.

Step 2
Graph the two functions using a TI-83 or similar graphing calculator.

Press $\boxed{Y =}$, and input the functions $Y_1 = |x^2 + x - 6| + |x|$ and $Y_2 = 4$ as shown in the given window.

Use the window settings of $x:[-10,10,1]$ and $y:[-10,10,1]$, and then press $\boxed{\text{GRAPH}}$ to obtain this window.

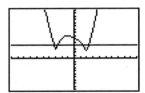

Step 3
Determine the points of intersection of the two graphs.

Press $\boxed{\text{2nd}}$ $\boxed{\text{TRACE}}$, and select 5:intersect to determine the points of intersection. At the points of intersection, the x-coordinates are approximately $x = -3.2$, $x = -2.7$, $x = 1.4$, and $x = 2.3$.

The solution set is $\{-3.2, -2.7, 1.4, 2.3\}$.

Topic Practice Questions

ANSWERS AND SOLUTIONS

1. **Step 1**
Perform the operation inside the last absolute value.
$|-2 - 1| = |-3|$

The expression simplifies to $|-6| + |9| \div |-3|$.

Step 2
Replace each absolute value with its equivalent positive number.
$|-6|+|9| \div |-3|$
$=(6)+(9) \div (3)$

Step 3
Perform the calculations following proper order of operations.
$(6)+(9) \div (3)$
$=6+3$
$=9$

The value of the expression $|-6|+|9| \div |-2-1|$ is 9.

2. **Step 1**
Perform all operations inside the absolute values.
$|6 \div 3|=|2| \qquad |-2 \times 5|=|-10|$

The expression simplifies to $|2|+|-4|-|-10|$.

Step 2
Replace each absolute value with its equivalent positive value.
$(2)+(4)-(10)$

Step 3
Evaluate the expression following proper order of operations.
$(2)+(4)-(10)$
$=6-10$
$=-4$

The value of $|6 \div 3|+|-4|-|-2 \times 5|$ is -4.

3. **Step 1**
Perform all operations inside the absolute values.
$|9 \div 3 \times 2|$
$=|3 \times 2|$
$=|6|$

$|-6-7|=|-13|$

The expression simplifies to $120+|6|-|-13|$.
Step 2
Replace each absolute value with its equivalent positive value.
$120+(6)-(13)$

Step 3
Evaluate the expression following proper order of operations.
$120+(6)-(13)$
$=126-13$
$=113$

The value of $120+|9 \div 3 \times 2|-|-6-7|$ is 113.

4. **Step 1**
Perform all operations inside the absolute values.
$|8 \times (-3)|=|-24| \quad |5-3|=|2|$

The expression simplifies to
$|-24|-|2|+|64| \div |-16|$.

Step 2
Replace each absolute value with its equivalent positive value.
$(24)-(2)+(64) \div (16)$

Step 3
Evaluate the expression following proper order of operations.
$(24)-(2)+(64) \div (16)$
$=24-2+4$
$=24+2$
$=26$

The value of $|8 \times (-3)|-|5-3|+|64| \div |-16|$ is 26.

5. **Step 1**
Apply the definition of an absolute value.
If $(-2x+9) \geq 0$, which means $x \leq \frac{9}{2}$,
then $|-2x+9|=-2x+9$.
If $(-2x+9) < 0$, which means $x > \frac{9}{2}$,
then $|-2x+9|=-(-2x+9)$.

Step 2
Express $y=|-2x+9|$ as a piecewise function.
$$y=\begin{cases} -2x+9, \ x \leq \frac{9}{2} \\ 2x-9, \ x > \frac{9}{2} \end{cases}$$

Step 3
Construct a table of values for the piecewise function.

$y = -2x + 9, x \le \dfrac{9}{2}$		$y = 2x - 9, x > \dfrac{9}{2},$	
x	y	x	y
$\dfrac{9}{2}$	0		
4	1	5	1
3	3	6	3
2	5	7	5
1	7	8	7
0	9	9	9

Step 4
Sketch the graph.

Plot the ordered pairs from the table of values on a Cartesian plane, and draw lines through the points to give a graph of the function.

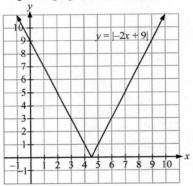

Step 5
State the intercepts and the domain and range of the function.

The graph of $y = |-2x + 9|$ intersects the x-axis at $\left(\dfrac{9}{2}, 0\right)$. The y-intercept is $(0, 9)$.

The domain is $x \in \mathbb{R}$, and the range is $y \ge 0$.

6.   Step 1
Let $f(x) = 3x^2 - 8$.

Sketch the graph of $f(x) = 3x^2 - 8$.

The graph of $f(x) = 3x^2 - 8$ can be sketched by stretching the graph of the parabola $y = x^2$ by a factor of 3 followed by a vertical translation 8 units down. Alternatively, a TI-83 or similar graphing calculator can be used.

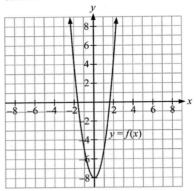

Step 2
Identify points where the graph of $y = f(x)$ is zero or positive (above the x-axis) and where the graph of $y = f(x)$ is negative (below the x-axis).

The function $f(x)$ is zero or positive when $x \le -1.6$ and $x \ge 1.6$. The function is negative when $-1.6 < x < 1.6$.

Step 3
Reflect the negative parts of $y = f(x)$ about the x-axis.

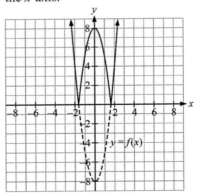

Step 4

Show the sketch of $y = |f(x)|$.

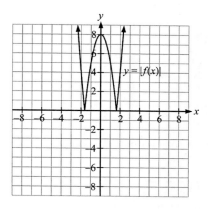

Step 5

State the intercepts and the domain and range of the function.

The graph of $y = |3x^2 - 8|$ intersects the x-axis at $(-1.6, 0)$ and $(1.6, 0)$. The y-intercept is $(0, 8)$.

The domain is $x \in \mathbb{R}$. The range of the function $y = |f(x)|$ is $y \ge 0$.

7.   Step 1

Apply the definition of an absolute value.

If $(4x - 3) \ge 0$, which means $x \ge \dfrac{3}{4}$,

then $|4x - 3| = 4x - 3$.

If $(4x - 3) < 0$, which means $x < \dfrac{3}{4}$,

then $|4x - 3| = -(4x - 3)$.

The outcome is two equations that are solved separately.

Step 2

Solve for x if $(4x - 3) \ge 0$.

$$|4x - 3| = 77$$
$$4x - 3 = 77$$
$$4x = 80$$
$$x = 20$$

Step 3

Solve for x if $(4x - 3) < 0$.

$$|4x - 3| = 77$$
$$-(4x - 3) = 77$$
$$4x - 3 = -77$$
$$4x = -74$$
$$x = -\frac{37}{2}$$

Step 4

Verify the solutions.

Both values appear to be valid because $x = 20$ satisfies $x \ge \dfrac{3}{4}$ and $x = -\dfrac{37}{2}$ satisfies $x < \dfrac{3}{4}$.

Substitute the solutions into the original equation to verify.

$x = 20$		$x = -\dfrac{37}{2}$	
LHS	**RHS**	**LHS**	**RHS**
$\begin{aligned}&\lvert 4(20) - 3\rvert\\ &\lvert 80 - 3\rvert\\ &\lvert 77\rvert\\ &77\end{aligned}$	77	$\begin{aligned}&\left\lvert 4\left(-\frac{37}{2}\right) - 3\right\rvert\\ &\lvert -74 - 3\rvert\\ &\lvert -77\rvert\\ &77\end{aligned}$	77

The solution set is $\left\{ 20, -\dfrac{37}{2} \right\}$.

8.   Step 1

Apply the definition of absolute value.

If $(x^2 - 6) \ge 0$, then $|x^2 - 6| = x^2 - 6$.
If $(x^2 - 6) < 0$, then $|x^2 - 6| = -(x^2 - 6)$.

The outcome is two equations that are solved separately.

Step 2

Solve for x if $(x^2 - 6) \ge 0$.

$$|x^2 - 6| = 10$$
$$x^2 - 6 = 10$$
$$x^2 = 16$$
$$x = \pm 4$$

Step 3

Solve for x if $(x^2 - 6) < 0$.

$$|x^2 - 6| = 10$$
$$-(x^2 - 6) = 10$$
$$x^2 - 6 = -10$$
$$x^2 = -4$$

Since the square root of a negative number is undefined, there is no solution when $(x^2 - 6) < 0$.

Step 4

Verify the solutions.

The possible solutions are $x = -4$ and $x = 4$.

Substitute the solutions into the original equation to verify.

$x = -4$		$x = 4$	
LHS	**RHS**	**LHS**	**RHS**
$\left|(-4)^2 - 6\right|$ $\left|16 - 6\right|$ 10	10	$\left|(4)^2 - 6\right|$ $\left|16 - 6\right|$ 10	10

The solution set is {–4, 4}.

9. **Step 1**

Break the equation into two separate functions.

Write the left side of the equation as Y_1 and the right side as Y_2.

$Y_1 = |9x - 2| + |x|$ and $Y_2 = 12$.

Step 2

Graph the two functions using a TI-83 or similar graphing calculator.

Press $\boxed{Y=}$, and input the functions $Y_1 = |9x - 2| + |x|$ and $Y_2 = 12$ as shown in the given window.

Use the window settings of $x : [-10, 10, 1]$ and $y : [-10, 20, 1]$, and then press $\boxed{\text{GRAPH}}$ to obtain this window.

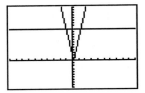

Step 3

Determine the points of intersection of the two graphs.

Press $\boxed{\text{2nd}}$ $\boxed{\text{TRACE}}$, and select 5:intersect to determine the points of intersection. At the points of intersection, the x-coordinates are $x = -1$ and $x = 1.4$.

Therefore, the solution set is {–1, 1.4}.

10. **Step 1**

Break the equation into two separate functions.

Write the left side of the equation as Y_1 and the right side as Y_2.

$Y_1 = |2x^2 - 15|$ and $Y_2 = 4x$.

Step 2

Graph the two functions using a TI-83 or similar graphing calculator.

Press $\boxed{Y=}$, and input the functions $Y_1 = |2x^2 - 15|$ and $Y_2 = 4x$ as shown in the given window.

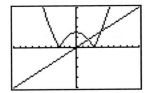

Use the window settings of $x : [-10, 10, 1]$ and $y : [-40, 40, 10]$, and then press $\boxed{\text{GRAPH}}$ to obtain this window.

Step 3
Determine the points of intersection of the two graphs.

Press $\boxed{\text{2nd}}$ $\boxed{\text{TRACE}}$, and select 5:intersect to determine the points of intersection.

At the points of intersection, the x-coordinates are approximately $x = 1.9$ and $x = 3.9$.

Therefore, the solution set is $\{1.9, 3.9\}$.

QUADRATIC FUNCTIONS AND EQUATIONS

Quadratic Functions in the Form $y = a(x-p)^2 + q$

PRACTICE EXERCISES
ANSWERS AND SOLUTIONS

1. The equation $y = \sqrt{x} + 5$ is equivalent to $y = x^{\frac{1}{2}} + 5$. A quadratic function can be written in the form $y = ax^2 + bx + c$, where a, b, and c are real numbers and $a \neq 0$. Therefore, $y = \sqrt{x} + 5$ is not a quadratic function since there is no degree two term.

2. Since $p(x) = (x+3)(x+4)$ becomes $p(x) = x^2 + 7x + 12$ when expanded, it is a quadratic function written in the form $p(x) = ax^2 + bx + c$, where $a = 1$, $b = 7$, and $c = 12$.

3. The function $y = x^2$ becomes $y = 3x^2$.

4. The function $y = x^2$ becomes $y = (x-9)^2 - 8$.

5. The function $y = x^2$ becomes $y = -x^2$.

6. The equation $y + 9 = (x+9)^2$ becomes $y = (x+9)^2 - 9$. There is a horizontal translation 9 units left and a vertical translation 9 units down.

7. The equation $2y = -6(x-5)^2 + 18$ becomes $y = -3(x-5)^2 + 9$. There is a vertical stretch about the x-axis by a factor of 3, a reflection in the x-axis, a horizontal translation 5 units right, and vertical translation 9 units up.

8. Step 1
Find $4f(x-1)$.

$$4f(x-1) = 4\left[\frac{1}{4}((x-1)+4)^2 - 11\right]$$

$$4f(x-1) = (x+3)^2 - 44$$

Step 2
Find $g(x)$.

$$g(x) = 4f(x-1) + 2$$

$$g(x) = ((x+3)^2 - 44) + 2$$

$$g(x) = (x+3)^2 - 42$$

Step 3
Find the y-intercept for $g(x)$.
Find $g(0)$.

$$g(0) = (0+3)^2 - 42$$

$$g(0) = 9 - 42$$

$$g(0) = -33$$

Therefore, the y-intercept for $g(x)$ is the point $(0, -33)$.

9. The vertex is $(-3, 5)$.
The axis of symmetry is $x = -3$.
The range is $y \le 5$.

The maximum value is $y = 5$.
The y-intercept is at $y = 2$.
The x-intercepts are at $x = -7$ and $x = 1$.

10. Step 1
Apply the transformations in the order shown.

i) $y = -x^2$

ii) $y = -\frac{2}{3}x^2$

iii) $y = -\frac{2}{3}(x+2)^2$

iv) $y = -\frac{2}{3}(x+2)^2 + 10$

Step 2
Find k.
Substitute 1 for x and k for y.

$$k = -\frac{2}{3}(1+2)^2 + 10$$

$$k = -\frac{2}{3}(3)^2 + 10$$

$$k = -\frac{2}{3}(9) + 10$$

$$k = -6 + 10$$

$$k = 4$$

The value of k is 4.

11. D
Step 1
Identify the transformations in the order of stretches and reflections followed by translations. If the function $f(x) = x^2$ is transformed to

$$g(x) = \frac{1}{2}(x+3)^2 + 4,$$ the following

transformations were applied to $f(x)$ in this order:

1) A vertical stretch about the x-axis by a factor of $\frac{1}{2}$

2) A horizontal translation 3 units left
3) A vertical translation 4 units up

Step 2
Find the new point on function g.
The original point $(2, 4)$ on function f would transform as follows:

1) $(2,4) \rightarrow (2,2)$ Multiply y by $\frac{1}{2}$.

2) $(2,2) \rightarrow (-1,2)$ Subtract 3 from x.

3) $(-1,2) \rightarrow (-1,6)$ Add 4 to y.

The point $(2, 4)$ on the graph of f would be transformed to the point $(-1, 6)$ on the graph of g.

12. Compared to the graph of $y = x^2$, the graph of $y = x^2 - 4$ has been vertically translated 4 units down. The vertex $(0, 0)$ of the graph of $y = x^2$ will now be at $(0, -4)$. The x-intercepts are at $x = -2$ and $x = 2$ (using technology).

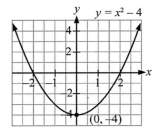

The graph of $-y = x^2 - 4$ is a reflection of the graph of $y = x^2 - 4$ about the x-axis ($y \to -y$). The y-intercept $(0, -4)$ on the graph of $y = x^2 - 4$ will be transformed to $(0, 4)$ on the graph of $-y = x^2 - 4$. The x-intercepts have not changed because at the x-axis the y-coordinate is 0, a value that remains unchanged with a reflection in the x-axis.

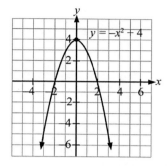

Quadratic Functions in the Form $y = ax^2 + bx + c$

ANSWERS AND SOLUTIONS

1. Expand and gather like terms to write the equation in the form $y = ax^2 + bx + c$.
$$y = 2(x+3)^2 + 5$$
$$y = 2(x+3)(x+3) + 5$$
$$y = 2(x^2 + 6x + 9) + 5$$
$$y = 2x^2 + 12x + 18 + 5$$
$$y = 2x^2 + 12x + 23$$

2. Expand and gather like terms to write the equation in the form $y = ax^2 + bx + c$.
$$3y = -\frac{3}{5}(x-5)^2 - 9$$
$$3y = -\frac{3}{5}(x-5)(x-5) - 9$$
$$3y = -\frac{3}{5}(x^2 - 10x + 25) - 9$$
$$3y = -\frac{3}{5}x^2 + \frac{30}{5}x - \frac{75}{5} - 9$$
$$3y = -\frac{3}{5}x^2 + 6x - 24$$
$$y = -\frac{1}{5}x^2 + 2x - 8$$

3. **Step 1**
    Factor the coefficient of the x^2-term out of the x^2- and x-terms only, and place those terms together in brackets.
    $$y = x^2 - 12x - 5$$
    $$y = (x^2 - 12x + \underline{\quad}) - 5$$

    Step 2
    Find the c-value of the perfect square trinomial using $\left[\frac{1}{2}(b)\right]^2$. Add and subtract this value inside the brackets.
    $$y = (x^2 - 12x + \underline{\quad}) - 5$$
    $$y = (x^2 - 12x + 36 - 36) - 5$$

    Step 3
    Multiply the subtracted term inside the brackets by a (the coefficient that was factored out), and move the result outside the brackets.
    $$y = (x^2 - 12x + 36 - 36) - 5$$
    $$y = (x^2 - 12x + 36) - 36(1) - 5$$

    Step 4
    Factor the perfect square trinomial in the brackets, and combine like terms outside the brackets.
    $$y = (x^2 - 12x + 36) - 36(1) - 5$$
    $$y = (x - 6)^2 - 41$$

4. **Step 1**
    Factor the coefficient of the x^2-term out of the x^2- and x-terms only, and place those terms together in brackets.
    $$y = -3x^2 + 12x - 1$$
    $$y = -3(x^2 - 4x + \underline{\quad}) - 1$$

    Step 2
    Find the c-value of the perfect square trinomial using $\left[\frac{1}{2}(b)\right]^2$. Add and subtract this value inside the brackets.
    $$y = -3(x^2 - 4x + \underline{\quad}) - 1$$
    $$y = -3(x^2 - 4x + 4 - 4) - 1$$

Step 3
Multiply the subtracted term inside the brackets by a (the coefficient that was factored out), and move the result outside the brackets.
$$y = -3\left(x^2 - 4x + 4 - 4\right) - 1$$
$$y = -3\left(x^2 - 4x + 4\right) - 4(-3) - 1$$

Step 4
Factor the perfect square trinomial in the brackets, and combine like terms outside the brackets.
$$y = -3\left(x^2 - 4x + 4\right) - 4(-3) - 1$$
$$y = -3(x-2)^2 + 11$$

5. **Step 1**
Factor the coefficient of the x^2-term out of the x^2- and x-terms only, and place those terms together in brackets.
$$y = \frac{1}{2}x^2 - 12x + 5$$
$$y = \frac{1}{2}\left(x^2 - 24x + \underline{\quad}\right) + 5$$

Step 2
Find the c-value of the perfect square trinomial using $\left[\frac{1}{2}(b)\right]^2$. Add and subtract this value inside the brackets.
$$y = \frac{1}{2}\left(x^2 - 24x + \underline{\quad}\right) + 5$$
$$y = \frac{1}{2}\left(x^2 - 24x + 144 - 144\right) + 5$$

Step 3
Multiply the subtracted term inside the brackets by a (the coefficient that was factored out), and move the result outside the brackets.
$$y = \frac{1}{2}\left(x^2 - 24x + 144 - 144\right) + 5$$
$$y = \frac{1}{2}\left(x^2 - 24x + 144\right) - 144\left(\frac{1}{2}\right) + 5$$

Step 4
Factor the perfect square trinomial in the brackets, and combine like terms outside the brackets.
$$y = \frac{1}{2}\left(x^2 - 24x + 144\right) - 144\left(\frac{1}{2}\right) + 5$$
$$y = \frac{1}{2}(x-12)^2 - 67$$

6. **Step 1**
Expand and then factor the coefficient of the x^2-term out of the x^2- and x-terms only, and place those terms together in brackets.
$$y = (x-8)(x+30)$$
$$y = x^2 + 22x - 240$$
$$y = \left(x^2 + 22x + \underline{\quad}\right) - 240$$

Step 2
Find the c-value of the perfect square trinomial using $\left[\frac{1}{2}(b)\right]^2$. Add and subtract this value inside the brackets.
$$y = \left(x^2 + 22x + \underline{\quad}\right) - 240$$
$$y = \left(x^2 + 22x + 121 - 121\right) - 240$$

Step 3
Multiply the subtracted term inside the brackets by a (the coefficient that was factored out), and move the result outside the brackets.
$$y = \left(x^2 + 22x + 121 - 121\right) - 240$$
$$y = \left(x^2 + 22x + 121\right) - 121(1) - 240$$

Step 4
Factor the perfect square trinomial in the brackets, and combine like terms outside the brackets.
$$y = \left(x^2 + 22x + 121\right) - 121(1) - 240$$
$$y = (x+11)^2 - 361$$

7. **Step 1**
Use $x = \dfrac{-b}{2a}$ to find the x-coordinate of the vertex.
$$x = \frac{-12}{2(-3)}$$
$$x = 2$$

Step 2
Solve for the y-coordinate of the vertex by substituting the x-coordinate into the equation of the original function.
$$y = -3(2)^2 + 12(2) - 1$$
$$y = -12 + 24 - 1$$
$$y = 11$$

The vertex is (2, 11).

8. **A**

Ronald's first mistake is in step 1 because $\dfrac{1}{4}$ should be correctly factored out of the x^2- and x-terms. The correct step should be

$$y = \frac{1}{4}\left(x^2 - 320x \qquad\right) + 11.$$

Applications of Quadratic Functions

ANSWERS AND SOLUTIONS

1. **Step 1**
Write an equation of the function that relates the income, I, to n, the number of weeks to wait until harvest.

In n weeks, the farmer will have $(1\,200 + 100n)$ bushels.

In n weeks, the price will be $\$(18 - 0.5n)$ per bushel.
$I = (\text{number of bushels})(\text{price per bushel})$
$I = (1\,200 + 100n)(18 - 0.5n)$

Step 2
Expand and complete the square for this function.
$I = (1\,200 + 100n)(18 - 0.5n)$
$I = -50n^2 + 1\,200n + 21\,600$
$I = -50\left(n^2 - 24n + \underline{\quad}\right) + 21\,600$
$I = -50\left(n^2 - 24n + 144 - 144\right) + 21\,600$
$I = -50\left(n^2 - 24n + 144\right) - 144(-50) + 21\,600$
$I = -50(n-12)^2 + 28\,800$

The vertex of the graph of the function is at (12, 28 800).

Therefore, the harvest should occur in 12 weeks when the maximum income is $28 800.

2. **a) Step 1**
Write the equation of the function that relates the income, I, to n, the number of students in excess of 75.

If n students over 75 are taken, there will be $(75 + n)$ students.

For n students over 75, the price per student will be $\$(6 - 0.05n)$ or $(600 - 5n)\text{¢}$.

$I = (\text{number of students})(\text{price per student})$
$I = (75 + n)(600 - 5n)$

Step 2
Expand and complete the square for this function.
$I = (75 + n)(600 - 5n)$
$I = -5n^2 + 225n + 45\,000$
$I = -5\left(n^2 - 45n + \underline{\quad}\right) + 45\,000$
$I = -5\left(n^2 - 45n + 506.25 - 506.25\right) + 45\,000$
$I = -5\left(n^2 - 45n + 506.25\right) - 506.25(-5) + 45\,000$
$I = -5(n - 22.5)^2 + 47\,531.25$

Step 3
Determine the number of students required to generate the maximum income.

The vertex of the graph of the function is at (22.5, 47 531.25). The maximum income would occur if the boat company took 22.5 extra students (over the 75). This is impossible because you cannot take half of a student.

Therefore, the company must transport 22 or 23 extra students to maximize their income (since the x-coordinate of the vertex is 22.5 and the parabola is symmetrical about its vertex, the value of the function when $n = 22$ will be the same as the value of the function when $n = 23$).

If $n = 22$, the number of students taken is $(75 + n) = 97$.
If $n = 23$, the number of students taken is $(75 + n) = 98$.

b) Determine the price per ticket if $n = 22$.
$(600 - 5n)$
$= 600 - 5(22)$
$= 490\text{¢}$
$= \$4.90$
The income would be $(97)(\$4.90) = \$475.30$.

Determine the price per ticket if $n = 23$.
The price per ticket is $(600 - 5n)$.

$$\left(600-5n\right)$$
$$=600-5\left(23\right)$$
$$=485¢$$
$$=\$4.85$$

The income would be $\left(98\right)\left(\$4.85\right)=\$475.30$.

The students should be charged either \$4.85 or \$4.90, depending on the number transported.

c) If either 97 or 98 students are taken, the maximum income would be \$475.30.

3. **Step 1**
Draw a diagram.
The diagram shows the street and the rectangular fence on three sides. It also shows the width, w, and the length, l.

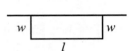

Step 2
Write an equation for the area, A, of the rectangle as a function of w.

Write the equation relating l and w.
$$2w+l=2\,500$$
$$l=2\,500-2w$$

Write the equation for the area, A.
$$A=\left(l\right)\left(w\right)$$
$$A=\left(2\,500-2w\right)\left(w\right)$$

Step 3
Expand and complete the square for this function.
$$A=\left(2\,500-2w\right)\left(w\right)$$
$$A=-2w^2+2\,500w$$
$$A=-2\left(w^2-1\,250w+\_\_\right)$$
$$A=-2\left(w^2-1\,250w+390\,625-390\,625\right)$$
$$A=-2\left(w^2-1\,250w+390\,625\right)-390\,625\left(-2\right)$$
$$A=-2\left(w-625\right)^2+781\,250$$

The vertex of the graph of this function is at (625, 781 250).

Step 4
Determine the maximum area and the dimensions that produce the maximum.

The maximum area is 781 250 m², which occurs when $w=625$ m.
$$l=\left(2\,500-2w\right)$$
$$l=\left(2\,500-2\left(625\right)\right)$$
$$l=1\,250\text{ m}$$

The maximum area of 781 250 m² occurs when the width is 625 m and the length is 1 250 m.

4. **Step 1**
Write the equation of a function that relates the sum, S, to one of the parts, x.

If x is one part, then $\left(20-x\right)$ will be the other part. Let S be the sum of the squares of the two parts.
$$S=x^2+\left(20-x\right)^2$$

Step 2
Expand and complete the square for this function.
$$S=x^2+\left(20-x\right)^2$$
$$S=x^2+400-40x+x^2$$

$$S=2x^2-40x+400$$
$$S=2\left(x^2-20x+\_\_\right)+400$$
$$S=2\left(x^2-20x+100-100\right)+400$$
$$S=2\left(x^2-20x+100\right)-100\left(2\right)+400$$
$$S=2\left(x-10\right)^2+200$$

Step 3
Determine the two parts.
The vertex of the graph of this function is at (10, 200). The minimum value of 200 occurs when $x=10$. The second part is $\left(20-x\right)=10$.

The two parts are 10 and 10.

You can confirm that the sum of the squares of these two parts is the minimum of 200.
$$10^2+10^2=200$$

5. **Step 1**
Draw a diagram.
The diagram shows a right triangle with hypotenuse h.

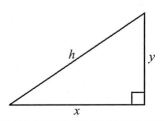

Step 2

Write the equation of a function that relates the length of the hypotenuse, h, to the length of side x. Write an equation relating x and y.

$$x + y = 40$$
$$y = 40 - x$$

Write an equation for the hypotenuse.

$$h^2 = x^2 + y^2$$
$$h^2 = x^2 + (40 - x)^2$$

Step 2

Expand and complete the square for this function.

$$h^2 = x^2 + (40 - x)^2$$
$$h^2 = x^2 + (40 - x)(40 - x)$$
$$h^2 = x^2 + 1\,600 - 80x + x^2$$
$$h^2 = 2x^2 - 80x + 1\,600$$
$$h^2 = 2(x^2 - 40x + \underline{}) + 1\,600$$
$$h^2 = 2(x^2 - 40x + 400 - 400) + 1\,600$$
$$h^2 = 2(x^2 - 40x + 400) - 400(2) + 1600$$
$$h^2 = 2(x - 20)^2 + 800$$

The vertex is at (20, 800).

The minimum value for h^2 is 800. If h^2 is a minimum, then h will also be a minimum. This minimum occurs when $x = 20$.

$$y = (40 - x)$$
$$y = (40 - 20)$$
$$y = 20$$

Therefore, each part of the string is 20 cm long.

6. Complete the square for the given function.

$$h(t) = 30t - 5t^2$$
$$h(t) = -5(t^2 - 6t + \underline{})$$
$$h(t) = -5(t^2 - 6t + 9 - 9)$$
$$h(t) = -5(t^2 - 6t + 9) - 9(-5)$$
$$h(t) = -5(t - 3)^2 + 45$$

The vertex is at (3, 45).

It takes 3 s for the baseball to reach its maximum height of 45 m.

Solving Quadratic Equations

ANSWERS AND SOLUTIONS

1. Solve the equation by factoring.
$$2x^2 + 5x - 12 = 0$$
$$2x^2 - 3x + 8x - 12 = 0$$
$$x(2x - 3) + 4(2x - 3) = 0$$
$$(2x - 3)(x + 4) = 0$$
$$2x - 3 = 0 \quad \text{or} \quad x + 4 = 0$$
$$2x = 3 \qquad\qquad x = -4$$
$$x = \frac{3}{2}$$

2. **Step 1**

Write the equation in the form $ax^2 + bx + c = 0$. Even though the variable used in the equation $\frac{2}{3}y^2 = 54$ is y, it can be solved exactly the same as if it involved x.

$$\frac{2}{3}y^2 = 54$$
$$\cancel{3}\left(\frac{2}{\cancel{3}}y^2\right) = 3(54)$$
$$2y^2 = 162$$
$$2y^2 - 162 = 0$$

Step 2
Solve by factoring.
$$2y^2 - 162 = 0$$
$$2(y^2 - 81) = 0$$
$$(y - 9)(y + 9) = 0$$

$$y - 9 = 0 \qquad y + 9 = 0$$
$$y = 9 \qquad\qquad y = -9$$

3. Solve by taking the square root of both sides of the equation.

$$\left(y+\frac{2}{3}\right)^2 = \frac{25}{9}$$

$$y+\frac{2}{3} = \pm\sqrt{\frac{25}{9}}$$

$$y+\frac{2}{3} = \pm\frac{5}{3}$$

$$y = -\frac{2}{3}\pm\frac{5}{3}$$

$$y = -\frac{7}{3} \text{ or } y = 1$$

4. **Step 1**

Write the equation in the form $ax^2+bx+c=0$.

$$b^2 = 7b+11$$
$$b^2-7b-11 = 0$$

Step 2

Complete the square.

$$b^2-7b = 11$$

$$b^2-7b+\frac{49}{4} = 11+\frac{49}{4}$$

$$\left(b-\frac{7}{2}\right)^2 = \frac{93}{4}$$

Step 3

Solve the equation by taking the square root of both sides of the equation.

$$\left(b-\frac{7}{2}\right)^2 = \frac{93}{4}$$

$$b-\frac{7}{2} = \pm\sqrt{\frac{93}{4}}$$

$$b-\frac{7}{2} = \pm\frac{\sqrt{93}}{2}$$

$$b = \frac{7}{2}\pm\frac{\sqrt{93}}{2}$$

$$b = \frac{7\pm\sqrt{93}}{2}$$

5. For an equation to have two real and equal roots, $b^2-4ac=0$.

Substitute the values of a, b, and c from the equation $3x^2-2x+c=0$ into the discriminant, and solve for c.

$$(-2)^2-4(3)(c) = 0$$
$$4-12c = 0$$
$$-12c = -4$$
$$c = \frac{-4}{-12}$$
$$c = \frac{1}{3}$$

6. Write the equation in the form $-\frac{q}{a} = (x-p)^2$.

$$0 = \frac{1}{2}(x-7)^2+5$$

$$-5 = \frac{1}{2}(x-7)^2$$

$$-10 = (x-7)^2$$

There is no real solution since the ratio $-\frac{q}{a}$ is negative. Taking the square root of both sides is not possible.

7. **Step 1**

Write the equation in the form $ax^2+bx+c=0$.

$$2y^2+11y = -15$$
$$2y^2+11y+15 = 0$$

Step 2

Solve the equation using the quadratic formula.

$$y = \frac{-11\pm\sqrt{11^2-4(2)(15)}}{2(2)}$$

$$y = \frac{-11\pm\sqrt{121-120}}{4}$$

$$y = \frac{-11\pm\sqrt{1}}{4}$$

$$y = \frac{-11+1}{4} \text{ or } y = \frac{-11-1}{4}$$

$$y = -\frac{10}{4} \text{ or } y = -\frac{12}{4}$$

$$y = -\frac{5}{2} \text{ or } y = -3$$

8. **Step 1**

Write the equation in the form $ax^2+bx+c=0$.

$$\frac{2x-1}{3} = \frac{x^2+2x}{5}$$

$$5(2x-1) = 3\left(x^2+2x\right)$$

$$10x-5 = 3x^2+6x$$

$$0 = 3x^2-4x+5$$

Step 2
Solve the equation using the quadratic formula.

$$x = \frac{-(-4) \pm \sqrt{(-4)^2 - 4(3)(5)}}{2(3)}$$

$$x = \frac{4 \pm \sqrt{16 - 60}}{6}$$

$$x = \frac{4 \pm \sqrt{-44}}{6}$$

This equation has no real roots since $b^2 - 4ac < 0$.

9. **Step 1**
Write a quadratic equation that represents the problem.

The points at which $y = 2x^2 + 4x + 2$ and $y = 6$ intersect will satisfy both equations.

Since the y-coordinate of these intersection points must be 6, substitute $y = 6$ into the equation $y = 2x^2 + 4x + 2$.

$$6 = 2x^2 + 4x + 2$$
$$0 = 2x^2 + 4x - 4$$
$$0 = 2(x^2 + 2x - 2)$$
$$0 = x^2 + 2x - 2$$

Step 2
Solve for the x-coordinates of the points of intersection using the quadratic formula.

$$x = \frac{-2 \pm \sqrt{2^2 - 4(1)(-2)}}{2(1)}$$

$$x = \frac{-2 \pm \sqrt{4 + 8}}{2}$$

$$x = \frac{-2 \pm \sqrt{12}}{2}$$

$$x = \frac{-2 \pm 2\sqrt{3}}{2}$$

$$x = -1 \pm \sqrt{3}$$

$$x = -1 + \sqrt{3} \text{ or } x = -1 - \sqrt{3}$$

10. **Step 1**
Write the function in the form $y = ax^2 + bx + c$.

$$y = (-3x - 2)(2x - 3)$$
$$y = -6x^2 + 5x + 6$$

Step 2
Find the vertex by completing the square.

$$y = -6\left(x^2 - \frac{5}{6}x + \underline{\quad}\right) + 6$$

$$y = -6\left(x^2 - \frac{5}{6}x + \frac{25}{144} - \frac{25}{144}\right) + 6$$

$$y = -6\left(x^2 - \frac{5}{6}x + \frac{25}{144}\right) - \frac{25}{144}(-6) + 6$$

$$y = -6\left(x - \frac{5}{12}\right)^2 + \frac{25}{24} + 6$$

$$y = -6\left(x - \frac{5}{12}\right)^2 + \frac{169}{24}$$

The vertex is at $\left(\dfrac{5}{12}, \dfrac{169}{24}\right)$.

Step 3
Find the y-intercept by substituting $x = 0$ into the equation $y = -6x^2 + 5x + 6$ and solving for y.

$$y = -6x^2 + 5x + 6$$
$$y = -6(0)^2 + 5(0) + 6$$
$$y = 6$$

The y-intercept is (0, 6).

Step 4
Find the x-intercepts by substituting $y = 0$ into the original equation, and solve each factor for x.

$$y = (-3x - 2)(2x - 3)$$
$$0 = (-3x - 2)(2x - 3)$$
$$-3x - 2 = 0 \quad \text{or} \quad 2x - 3 = 0$$
$$-3x = 2 \quad \text{or} \quad 2x = 3$$
$$x = -\frac{2}{3} \quad \text{or} \quad x = \frac{3}{2}$$

The x-intercepts are $\left(-\dfrac{2}{3}, 0\right)$ and $\left(\dfrac{3}{2}, 0\right)$.

11. **Step 1**
Use the given zeros to write the function in the form $y = a(x - s)(x - t)$, and expand.

Let $s = -3$ and $t = 4$.

$$y = a(x - (-3))(x - 4)$$
$$y = a(x + 3)(x - 4)$$
$$y = a(x^2 - x - 12)$$

Step 2

Find the value of a by substituting the coordinates of the given point for x and y. Substitute $x = 5$ and $y = 8$.

$$y = a(x^2 - x - 12)$$
$$8 = a((5)^2 - (5) - 12)$$
$$8 = 8a$$
$$1 = a$$

Step 3

Write the equation of the function in the form $y = ax^2 + bx + c$.

Substitute the value for a into $y = a(x^2 - x - 12)$, and expand.

$$y = 1(x^2 - x - 12)$$
$$y = x^2 - x - 12$$

Applications of Quadratic Equations

ANSWERS AND SOLUTIONS

1. **Step 1**

   Substitute the given information into the quadratic equation, and write it in the form $ax^2 + bx + c = 0$.

   $$h(t) = -5t^2 + 30t + 1$$
   $$41 = -5t^2 + 30t + 1$$
   $$0 = -5t^2 + 30t - 40$$

   Step 2

   Solve the equation by factoring.

   $$0 = -5t^2 + 30t - 40$$
   $$0 = -5(t^2 - 6t + 8)$$
   $$0 = (t - 4)(t - 2)$$
   $$t - 4 = 0 \quad \text{or} \quad t - 2 = 0$$
   $$t = 4 \qquad\qquad t = 2$$

   The ball reaches a height of 41 m at $t = 2$ s and at $t = 4$ s.

2. **Step 1**

   Write a quadratic equation in the form $ax^2 + bx + c = 0$.

   If x is one number, then $x + 2\sqrt{2}$ is the other number. Their product is 2.

   $$x(x + 2\sqrt{2}) = 2$$
   $$x^2 + 2\sqrt{2}(x) = 2$$
   $$x^2 + 2\sqrt{2}(x) - 2 = 0$$

   (Note: It is also possible to define the two numbers as x and $x - 2\sqrt{2}$).

   Step 2

   Solve the equation using the quadratic formula.

   $$x = \frac{-2\sqrt{2} \pm \sqrt{(2\sqrt{2})^2 - 4(1)(-2)}}{2(1)}$$
   $$x = \frac{-2\sqrt{2} \pm \sqrt{8 + 8}}{2}$$
   $$x = \frac{-2\sqrt{2} \pm \sqrt{16}}{2}$$
   $$x = \frac{-2\sqrt{2} \pm 4}{2}$$
   $$x = -\sqrt{2} \pm 2$$

   Since x must be positive, $x = -\sqrt{2} + 2$ only.

   Determine the other number if $x = -\sqrt{2} + 2$.

   $$x + 2\sqrt{2}$$
   $$= -\sqrt{2} + 2 + 2\sqrt{2}$$
   $$= 2 + \sqrt{2}$$

   The two numbers are $-\sqrt{2} + 2$ and $2 + \sqrt{2}$.

3. **Step 1**

   Write a quadratic equation in the form $ax^2 + bx + c = 0$ using the area formula for a rectangle.

   If w is the width and l is the length of the rectangle, then the sum of the length and width can be written as $l + w = 19$.

   The area is 60 m^2.

   $$A = lw$$
   $$60 = (19 - w)w$$
   $$60 = 19w - w^2$$
   $$w^2 - 19w + 60 = 0$$

   Step 2

   Solve the equation by factoring.

   $$w^2 - 19w + 60 = 0$$
   $$(w - 15)(w - 4) = 0$$

$w-15=0$ or $w-4=0$
$\quad w=15 \qquad w=4$

Determine l if $w=4$.
$l=19-w$
$l=19-4$
$l=15$

The rectangle has a width of 4 m and a length of 15 m. (Alternatively, if $w=15$, $l=4$.)

Topic Practice Questions

ANSWERS AND SOLUTIONS

1. The function $y=x^2$ becomes $y=\dfrac{1}{2}x^2$, which then becomes $y=-\dfrac{1}{2}x^2$. Then, $y=-\dfrac{1}{2}x^2$ becomes $y=-\dfrac{1}{2}(x-3)^2-1$.

2. **Step 1**
    Write the function in $y=a(x-p)^2+q$ form.

    Solve for y by dividing both sides by 3.
    $3y=(x-5)^2-6$
    $\dfrac{3}{3}y=\dfrac{(x-5)^2}{3}-\dfrac{6}{3}$
    $y=\dfrac{1}{3}(x-5)^2-2$

    Step 2
    Apply the transformations in the order of stretches and reflections, followed by translations.
    The graph of $y=x^2$ is transformed to the graph of $y=\dfrac{1}{3}x^2$ by applying a vertical stretch about the x-axis by a factor of $\dfrac{1}{3}$.

    Then, the graph of $y=\dfrac{1}{3}x^2$ is transformed to the graph of $y=\dfrac{1}{3}(x-5)^2-2$ by translating the graph 5 units to the right and 2 units down.

3. **Step 1**
    Find the vertex of the graph of the function $y=(x-0.5)^2-6.25$ using transformations.

    Compared to $y=x^2$, the parabola is horizontally translated 0.5 units to the right and vertically translated 6.25 units down.

    Therefore, vertex $(0, 0)$ on the graph of $y=x^2$ becomes $(0.5, -6.25)$ on the graph of $y=(x-0.5)^2-6.25$.

    Step 2
    Identify the characteristics of the transformed parabola.

    If the vertex of the graph of $y=(x-0.5)^2-6.25$ is $(0.5, -6.25)$, the axis of symmetry is $x=0.5$. The domain is $x \in \mathbb{R}$. Since $a>0$, the parabola opens up. The range is $y \geq -6.25$. The function has a minimum y-value of -6.25.

    Step 3
    Find the intercepts.

    Substitute $x=0$, and solve for y to find the y-intercept.
    $y=(x-0.5)^2-6.25$
    $y=(0-0.5)^2-6.25$
    $y=0.25-6.25$
    $y=-6$

    The y-intercept is $(0, -6)$.

    Substitute $y=0$, and solve for x to find the x-intercepts.
    $$y=(x-0.5)^2-6.25$$
    $$0=(x-0.5)^2-6.25$$
    $$6.25=(x-0.5)^2$$
    $$\pm 2.5=x-0.5$$
    $$0.5\pm 2.5=x$$
    $$3=x$$
    $$-2=x \text{ and } 3=x$$

    The x-intercepts are $(3, 0)$ and $(-2, 0)$.

    Step 4
    Sketch the graph of the function $y=(x-0.5)^2-6.25$.
    Plot the vertex and intercepts.

The graph of $y = (x - 0.5)^2 - 6.25$ is shown.

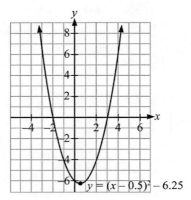

4. **Step 1**
Substitute the known values into the equation $y = a(x - p)^2 + q$.

Since the vertex is (–2, –5), $p = -2$ and $q = -5$. If one of the x-intercepts is –3, this means the parabola contains the point (–3, 0).
$$y = a(x - p)^2 + q$$
$$y = a(x + 2)^2 - 5$$
$$0 = a(-3 + 2)^2 - 5$$

Step 2
Solve for a.
$$0 = a(-3 + 2)^2 - 5$$
$$0 = a(-1)^2 - 5$$
$$0 = a - 5$$
$$5 = a$$

Therefore, the equation of the parabola is
$$y = 5(x + 2)^2 - 5.$$

Step 3
Write the function in the form $y = ax^2 + bx + c$ by expanding.
$$y = 5(x + 2)^2 - 5$$
$$y = 5(x^2 + 4x + 4) - 5$$
$$y = 5x^2 + 20x + 20 - 5$$
$$y = 5x^2 + 20x + 15$$

Alternate solution:
Step 1
Write the function in the form $y = a(x - s)(x - t)$.

Substitute the values of $s = -3$ and $t = -1$.
$$y = a(x - (-3))(x - (-1))$$
$$y = a(x + 3)(x + 1)$$
$$y = a(x^2 + 4x + 3)$$

Step 2
Find the value of a by substituting the coordinates of the vertex into $y = a(x^2 + 4x + 3)$.

Substitute $x = -2$ and $y = -5$ into the equation.
$$y = a(x^2 + 4x + 3)$$
$$-5 = a((-2)^2 + 4(-2) + 3)$$
$$-5 = -a$$
$$5 = a$$

Step 3
Write the function in the form $y = ax^2 + bx + c$.
Substitute the value for a into $y = a(x^2 + 4x + 3)$, and expand.
$$y = 5(x^2 + 4x + 3)$$
$$y = 5x^2 + 20x + 15$$

5. **Step 1**
Write the equation of the function in the form $y = a(x - p) + q$ by completing the square.
$$y = x^2 + 8x + 18$$
$$y = (x^2 + 8x + \underline{\quad}) + 18$$
$$y = (x^2 + 8x + 16 - 16) + 18$$
$$y = (x^2 + 8x + 16) - 16(1) + 18$$
$$y = (x + 4)^2 + 2$$

Step 2
Identify the characteristics of the function.
The vertex is (–4, 2). The axis of symmetry is $x = -4$. The domain is $x \in \mathbb{R}$. The range is $y \geq 2$.
The parabola opens upward since $a > 0$.
The minimum value of y is 2.

Substitute $x = 0$, and solve for y to find the y-intercept. (You can use the equation in either form.)
$$y = x^2 + 8x + 18$$
$$y = 0^2 + 8(0) + 18$$
$$y = 18$$

The y-intercept is (0, 18).

Substitute $y = 0$, and solve for x to find the x-intercepts. (You can use the equation in either form.)

$$y = (x+4)^2 + 2$$
$$0 = (x+4)^2 + 2$$
$$-2 = (x+4)^2$$
$$\pm\sqrt{-2} = x + 4$$

There are no x-intercepts since it is not possible to take the square root of a negative.

6. **Step 1**
Find the value of a using the vertex formula. The x-coordinate of the vertex is determined from $x = \dfrac{-b}{2a}$.

Use the given equation $y = ax^2 - 8x + c$ and the coordinates of the vertex $(-4, 2)$.

$$x = \frac{-b}{2a}$$
$$-4 = \frac{-(-8)}{2a}$$
$$-4 = \frac{8}{2a}$$
$$-8a = 8$$
$$a = -1$$

Step 2
Find the value of c by substituting the value of a and the coordinates of the vertex into the given equation. Substitute $a = -1$, $x = -4$, and $y = 2$ into $y = ax^2 - 8x + c$.

$$y = ax^2 - 8x + c$$
$$y = -x^2 - 8x + c$$
$$2 = -(-4)^2 - 8(-4) + c$$
$$2 = -16 + 32 + c$$
$$2 = 16 + c$$
$$-14 = c$$

Therefore, $a = -1$ and $c = -14$.

7. **Step 1**
Write the equation in the form $y = ax^2 + bx + c$.

$$\frac{-3x^2 + 5}{2} = x - 1$$
$$2\left(\frac{-3x^2 + 5}{2}\right) = 2(x-1)$$
$$-3x^2 + 5 = 2(x) - 2(1)$$
$$-3x^2 + 5 = 2x - 2$$
$$0 = 3x^2 + 2x - 7$$

Step 2
Solve the equation using the quadratic formula.

$$x = \frac{-b \pm \sqrt{b^2 - 4ac}}{2a}$$
$$x = \frac{-2 \pm \sqrt{(2)^2 - 4(3)(-7)}}{2(3)}$$
$$x = \frac{-2 \pm \sqrt{88}}{6}$$
$$x = \frac{-2 \pm 2\sqrt{22}}{6}$$
$$x = \frac{-1 \pm \sqrt{22}}{3}$$

Therefore, $x = \dfrac{-1 + \sqrt{22}}{3}$ or $x = \dfrac{-1 - \sqrt{22}}{3}$.

8. **Step 1**
Use the given zeros to write the equation of the function in the form $a(x-s)(x-t) = 0$, and expand.
$s = -3$ and $t = 8$

$$a(x - (-3))(x - 8) = y$$
$$a(x + 3)(x - 8) = y$$
$$a(x^2 - 8x + 3x - 24) = y$$
$$a(x^2 - 5x - 24) = y$$

Step 2
Solve for a by substituting the coordinates of the given point for x and y. Substitute $x = 1$ and $y = 1$ into $a(x^2 - 5x - 24) = y$, and solve for a.

$$a(x^2 - 5x - 24) = y$$
$$a((1)^2 - 5(1) - 24) = 1$$
$$-28a = 1$$
$$a = -\frac{1}{28}$$

Step 3
Write the equation in the form $y = ax^2 + bx + c$.
Substitute the value for a into $a(x^2 - 5x - 24) = y$,
and expand.

$$a(x^2 - 5x - 24) = y$$
$$-\frac{1}{28}(x^2 - 5x - 24) = y$$
$$-\frac{1}{28}x^2 + \frac{5}{28}x + \frac{24}{28} = y$$
$$-\frac{1}{28}x^2 + \frac{5}{28}x + \frac{6}{7} = y$$

9. **Step 1**
Write the equation in the form $ax^2 + bx + c = 0$.
$$2x^2 - kx = -6$$
$$2x^2 - kx + 6 = 0$$

Step 2
Find the values of k. For the equation to have real and equal roots, the discriminant must equal 0.
$$b^2 - 4ac = 0$$
$$(-k)^2 - 4(2)(6) = 0$$
$$k^2 - 48 = 0$$
$$k^2 = 48$$
$$k = \pm\sqrt{48}$$
$$k = \pm 4\sqrt{3}$$

Therefore, $k = 4\sqrt{3}$ or $k = -4\sqrt{3}$.

10. Let n represent the number of $1.00 increases in the price of a ticket, and let R represent the revenue from the ticket sales.

a) Determine the revenue as a function of the number of price increases.
$$R = (\text{number of tickets})(\text{price per ticket})$$
$$R = (6\,000 - 200n)(20 + n)$$
$$R = -200n^2 + 2\,000n + 120\,000$$

b) To find the maximum revenue, R, complete the square.
$$R = -200(n^2 - 10n + \underline{\quad}) + 120\,000$$
$$R = -200(n^2 - 10n + 25 - 25) + 120\,000$$
$$R = -200(n^2 - 10n + 25) - 25(-200) + 120\,000$$
$$R = -200(n - 5)^2 + 125\,000$$

The vertex is at (5, 125 000).

Therefore, the ticket price will be
$\$(20 + n) = \$(20 + 5)$, which is $25.
(There should be five increases of $1.00)

c) The maximum revenue is $125 000 as given by the y-coordinate of the vertex.

11. **Step 1**
Draw a diagram.
Let x represent the length of one leg, and let $x + 6$ represent the length of the other leg.

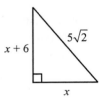

Step 2
Write a quadratic equation in the form $ax^2 + bx + c = 0$ using the Pythagorean theorem to relate the lengths of all three sides of the right triangle.
$$x^2 + (x + 6)^2 = (5\sqrt{2})^2$$
$$x^2 + x^2 + 12x + 36 = 50$$
$$2x^2 + 12x - 14 = 0$$

Step 3
Solve the equation by factoring.
$$2x^2 + 12x - 14 = 0$$
$$2(x^2 + 6x - 7) = 0$$
$$2(x - 1)(x + 7) = 0$$
$$x - 1 = 0 \text{ or } x + 7 = 0$$
$$x = 1 \qquad\qquad x = -7$$

Since x must be positive, $x = 1$.

Therefore, the lengths of the two legs are 1 cm and $1 + 6 = 7$ cm.

12. a) The height of the building will be the height of the rock at $t = 0$.
$$h(0) = -5(0)^2 + 10(0) + 15$$
$$h(0) = 15$$

The height of the building is 15 m.

b) The rock is in the air until it hits the ground.
Solve the equation for t when $h(t) = 0$.

$$h(t) = -5t^2 + 10t + 15$$
$$0 = -5t^2 + 10t + 15$$
$$0 = 5t^2 - 10t - 15$$
$$0 = 5(t^2 - 2t - 3)$$
$$0 = 5(t+1)(t-3)$$
$$t+1 = 0 \quad \text{or} \quad t-3 = 0$$
$$t = -1 \qquad t = 3$$

Since $t \geq 0$, $t = 3$ only.
The height is 0 m at $t = 3$ s.

The rock is in the air for 3 s.

c) Find how long it takes the rock to reach its maximum height by completing the square and identifying the vertex of the graph of the function.

$$h(t) = -5t^2 + 10t + 15$$
$$h(t) = -5(t^2 - 2t \ \underline{\quad}) + 15$$
$$h(t) = -5(t^2 - 2t + 1) - (1)(-5) + 15$$
$$h(t) = -5(t-1)^2 + 20$$

The vertex is at (1, 20). The rock reaches its maximum height 1 s after it is thrown.

d) Since the y-coordinate of the vertex is 20, the maximum height reached by the rock is 20 m.

LINEAR AND QUADRATIC SYSTEMS

Solving a System of Equations Graphically

ANSWERS AND SOLUTIONS

1. **Step 1**
Graph the functions represented by the given equations.

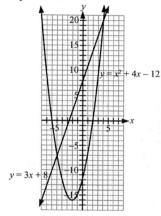

Step 2
Determine the points of intersection.

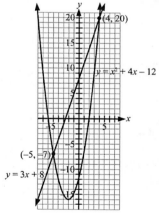

From the graph, it can be seen that the points of intersection are at (−5, −7) and (4, 20).

The solution set for the system is {(−5, −7), (4, 20)}.

2. **Step 1**
Graph the functions represented by the given equations.

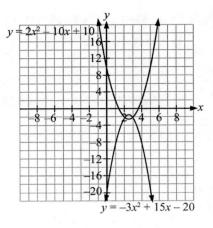

Step 2
Determine the points of intersection.

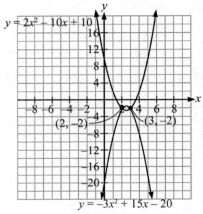

From the graph, it can be seen that the points of intersection are at (2, –2) and (3, –2).

The solution set for the system is {(2, –2), (3, –2)}.

3. **Step 1**
Graph the functions represented by the given equations using a graphing calculator.

Press $\boxed{Y=}$, and input each function.
$Y_1 = (3x-5)(2x+1)$
$Y_2 = 2x^2 - 7x$

Press $\boxed{GRAPH}$. The window setting used to display the two graphs is $x:[-3,5,1]$ and $y:[-10,15,1]$.

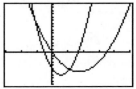

Step 2
Find the points of intersection.

Press $\boxed{2nd}$ $\boxed{TRACE}$, and choose 5:intersect.

For "First curve?", position the cursor just left or right of the intersection point that is farthest to the left, and press $\boxed{ENTER}$.

For "Second curve?", position the cursor just left or right of the intersection point that is farthest to the left, and press $\boxed{ENTER}$.

For "Guess?", press $\boxed{ENTER}$.

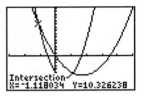

Repeat the process with the intersection point that is farthest to the right.

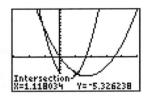

The calculator indicates that the points of intersection of the two curves are at (–1.12, 10.33) and (1.12, –5.33).

The solution set for the system of equations is {(–1.12, 10.33), (1.12, –5.33)}.

4. **Step 1**
Write the second equation in the form $y = mx + b$.
$0 = 6x + y + 1$
$-y = 6x + 1$
$y = -6x - 1$

Step 2
Graph the functions represented by the given equations using a graphing calculator.

Press $\boxed{Y=}$, and input each function.
$Y_1 = x^2 - 2x + 3$
$Y_2 = -6x - 1$

Press $\boxed{GRAPH}$. The window setting used to

display the two graphs is $x:[-5,5,1]$ and $y:[-5,20,2]$.

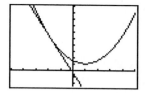

Step 3
Find the point of intersection.

Press [2nd] [TRACE], and choose 5:intersect.

For "First curve?", position the cursor just left or right of the intersection point, and press [ENTER].

For "Second curve?", position the cursor just left or right of the intersection point, and press [ENTER].

For "Guess?", press [ENTER].

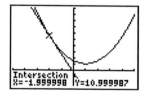

The calculator indicates that the point of intersection of the curve and the line is (–2.00, 11.00).

The solution set for the system of equations is {(–2.00, 11.00)}.

5. **Step 1**
Write the first equation in the form $y = ax^2 + bx + c$.

$y + 9x = 3x^2 - 1$
$\quad y = 3x^2 - 9x - 1$

Step 2
Graph the functions represented by the given equations using a graphing calculator.

Press [Y=], and input each function.
$\quad Y_1 = 3x^2 - 9x - 1$
$\quad Y_2 = -2x^2 + 7$

Press [GRAPH]. The window setting used to

display the two graphs is $x:[-5,5,1]$ and $y:[-10,10,1]$.

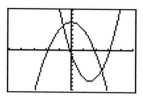

Step 3
Find the points of intersection.

Press [2nd] [TRACE], and choose 5:intersect.

For "First curve?", position the cursor just left or right of the intersection point that is farthest to the left, and press [ENTER].

For "Second curve?", position the cursor just left or right of the intersection point that is farthest to the left, and press [ENTER].

For "Guess?", press [ENTER].

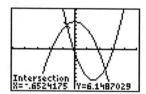

Repeat the process with the intersection point that is farthest to the right.

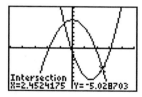

The calculator indicates that the points of intersection of the two curves are at (–0.65, 6.15) and (2.45, –5.03).

The solution set for the system of equations is {(–0.65, 6.15), (2.45, –5.03)}.

6. **Step 1**
Write the first equation in the form $y = mx + b$ and the second equation in the form $y = ax^2 + bx + c$.

$y - 4x = -3$
$\quad y = 4x - 3$

$8x^2 - 3 = -5x - y$
$\quad y = -8x^2 - 5x + 3$

Step 2
Graph the functions represented by the given equations using a graphing calculator.

Press $\boxed{Y=}$, and input each function.
$Y_1 = 4x - 3$
$Y_2 = -8x^2 - 5x + 3$

Press $\boxed{\text{GRAPH}}$. The window setting used to display the two graphs is $x : [-5, 5, 1]$ and $y : [-15, 5, 1]$.

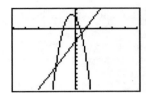

Step 3
Find the points of intersection.

Press $\boxed{\text{2nd}}$ $\boxed{\text{TRACE}}$, and choose 5:intersect.

For "First curve?", position the cursor just left or right of the intersection point that is farthest to the left, and press $\boxed{\text{ENTER}}$.

For "Second curve?", position the cursor just left or right of the intersection point that is farthest to the left, and press $\boxed{\text{ENTER}}$.

For "Guess?", press $\boxed{\text{ENTER}}$.

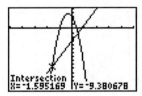

Repeat the process with the intersection point that is farthest to the right.

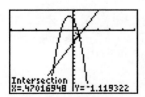

The calculator indicates that the points of intersection of the curve and the line are at $(-1.60, -9.38)$ and $(0.47, -1.12)$.

The solution set for the system of equations is $\{(-1.60, -9.38), (0.47, -1.12)\}$.

Solving a System of Equations Algebraically

ANSWERS AND SOLUTIONS

1. **Step 1**
Isolate one variable from equation 1 or 2.

In this case, both equations already have the y-variable isolated.

Step 2
Substitute the expression represented by the isolated variable from equation 2 into equation 1, and simplify.

Substitute $-4x - 25$ for y into equation 1, and bring all terms to one side.
$$x^2 - 35x + 5 = y$$
$$x^2 - 35x + 5 = -4x - 25$$
$$x^2 - 31x + 30 = 0$$

Step 3
Solve for x by factoring the quadratic equation.
$$x^2 - 31x + 30 = 0$$
$$x^2 - 30x - x + 30 = 0$$
$$x(x - 30) - 1(x - 30) = 0$$
$$(x - 30)(x - 1) = 0$$
$$x - 30 = 0 \qquad x - 1 = 0$$
$$x = 30 \qquad x = 1$$

Step 4
Substitute the solved values of x into equation 2, and solve for y.

$y = -4x - 25$	$y = -4x - 25$
$y = -4(30) - 25$	$y = -4(1) - 25$
$y = -120 - 25$	$y = -4 - 25$
$y = -145$	$y = -29$

Step 5
Write the solutions as ordered pairs in set notation.
$\{(30, -145), (1, -29)\}$

2. **Step 1**
Isolate one variable from equation 1 or 2.

In this case, equation 1 has the y-variable isolated.

Step 2
Substitute the expression represented by the isolated variable into equation 2, and simplify.

Substitute $3-6x$ for y in equation 2, and bring all terms to one side.
$$2x^2 + 8x = 3 - y$$
$$2x^2 + 8x = 3 - (3 - 6x)$$
$$2x^2 + 8x = 3 - 3 + 6x$$
$$2x^2 + 8x = 6x$$
$$2x^2 + 2x = 0$$

Step 3
Solve for x by factoring the quadratic equation.
$$2x^2 + 2x = 0$$
$$2x(x + 1) = 0$$
$$2x = 0 \qquad x + 1 = 0$$
$$x = 0 \qquad\quad x = -1$$

Step 4
Substitute the solved values of x into equation 1, and solve for y.
$$y = 3 - 6x \qquad\qquad y = 3 - 6x$$
$$y = 3 - 6(0) \qquad\quad y = 3 - 6(-1)$$
$$y = 3 \qquad\qquad\qquad y = 3 + 6$$
$$\qquad\qquad\qquad\qquad y = 9$$

Step 5
Write the solutions as ordered pairs in set notation.
$\{(0, 3), (-1, 9)\}$

3. **Step 1**
Isolate one variable from equation 1 or 2.

Isolate the y-variable in equation 2.
$$-4x^2 - x = y + 3$$
$$y = -4x^2 - x - 3$$

Step 2
Substitute the expression represented by the isolated variable from equation 2 into equation 1, and simplify.

Substitute $-4x^2 - x - 3$ for y in equation 1, and bring all terms to one side.

$$x = 5x^2 + y - 32$$
$$x = 5x^2 + (-4x^2 - x - 3) - 32$$
$$x = 5x^2 - 4x^2 - x - 3 - 32$$
$$x = x^2 - x - 35$$
$$0 = x^2 - 2x - 35$$

Step 3
Solve for x by factoring the quadratic equation.
$$0 = x^2 - 2x - 35$$
$$0 = (x - 7)(x + 5)$$
$$x - 7 = 0 \qquad x + 5 = 0$$
$$x = 7 \qquad\quad x = -5$$

Step 4
Substitute the solved values of x into equation 1, and solve for y.
$$x = 5x^2 + y - 32 \qquad\qquad x = 5x^2 + y - 32$$
$$7 = 5(7)^2 + y - 32 \qquad\quad -5 = 5(-5)^2 + y - 32$$
$$7 = 245 + y - 32 \qquad\qquad -5 = 125 + y - 32$$
$$-238 = y - 32 \qquad\qquad\quad -130 = y - 32$$
$$-206 = y \qquad\qquad\qquad\quad -98 = y$$

Step 5
Write the solutions as ordered pairs in set notation.
$\{(-5, -98), (7, -206)\}$

4. **Step 1**
Add equation 1 and equation 2 to eliminate the y-variable.
$$① \;\; -x^2 + y = 4x - 4$$
$$② \;\; \underline{-5x - y = -6}$$
$$-x^2 - 5x = 4x - 10$$

Step 2
Solve for x.
$$-x^2 - 5x = 4x - 10$$
$$0 = x^2 + 9x - 10$$
$$0 = (x - 1)(x + 10)$$
$$x - 1 = 0 \qquad x + 10 = 0$$
$$x = 1 \qquad\quad x = -10$$

Step 3
Substitute the solved values of x into equation 2, and solve for y.
$$-5x - y = -6 \qquad\qquad -5x - y = -6$$
$$-5(1) - y = -6 \qquad\quad -5(-10) - y = -6$$
$$-5 - y = -6 \qquad\qquad 50 - y = -6$$
$$-y = -1 \qquad\qquad\quad -y = -56$$
$$y = 1 \qquad\qquad\qquad y = 56$$

Step 4
Write the solutions as ordered pairs in set notation.
$\{(1, 1), (-10, 56)\}$

5. **Step 1**
Multiply equation 2 by 3.
②×3 $3(y + 4x = 3) \rightarrow 3y + 12x = 9$

Let $3y + 12x = 9$ represent equation 3.

Step 2
Subtract equation 3 from equation 1 to eliminate y.
① $\;\;3y + 3x = 3x^2 + 15$
③ $\;\;3y + 12x = 9$
$$\overline{\quad\quad -9x = 3x^2 + 6}$$

Step 3
Solve for x.
$-9x = 3x^2 + 6$
$0 = 3x^2 + 9x + 6$
$0 = 3(x^2 + 3x + 2)$
$0 = x^2 + 3x + 2$
$0 = (x + 1)(x + 2)$
$x + 1 = 0 \qquad x + 2 = 0$
$\quad\; x = -1 \qquad\quad x = -2$

Step 4
Substitute the solved values of x into equation 2, and solve for y.
$$\begin{array}{ll} y + 4x = 3 & y + 4x = 3 \\ y + 4(-1) = 3 & y + 4(-2) = 3 \\ y - 4 = 3 & y - 8 = 3 \\ y = 7 & y = 11 \end{array}$$

Step 5
Write the solutions as ordered pairs in set notation.
$\{(-1, 7), (-2, 11)\}$

6. **Step 1**
Subtract equation 2 from equation 1 to eliminate the y-variable.
① $\quad \dfrac{1}{2}x^2 - 172 = y + 33x$
② $\quad -\dfrac{3}{2}x^2 + 17x = y - 128$
$$\overline{2x^2 - 172 - 17x = 33x + 128}$$

Step 2
Solve for x.
$2x^2 - 172 - 17x = 33x + 128$
$2x^2 - 50x - 300 = 0$
$2(x^2 - 25x - 150) = 0$
$2(x - 30)(x + 5) = 0$
$(x - 30)(x + 5) = 0$
$$\begin{array}{ll} x - 30 = 0 & x + 5 = 0 \\ \quad\;\; x = 30 & \quad\;\; x = -5 \end{array}$$

Step 3
Substitute the solved values of x into equation 1, and solve for y.
$\dfrac{1}{2}x^2 - 172 = y + 33x$
$\dfrac{1}{2}(30)^2 - 172 = y + 33(30)$
$450 - 172 = y + 990$
$278 = y + 990$
$-712 = y$

$\dfrac{1}{2}x^2 - 172 = y + 33x$
$\dfrac{1}{2}(-5)^2 - 172 = y + 33(-5)$
$\dfrac{25}{2} - 172 = y - 165$
$-\dfrac{319}{2} = y - 165$
$\dfrac{11}{2} = y$

Step 4
Write the solutions as ordered pairs in set notation.
$\left\{ (30, -712), \left(-5, \dfrac{11}{2}\right) \right\}$

7. **Step 1**
Set up a system of two equations.

The difference between y and 12 times x can be represented by $y - 12x = -69$.

The difference between y and the square of x is represented by $y - x^2 = -33$.

The system of equations is as follows:
① $\quad y - 12x = -69$
② $\quad y - x^2 = -33$

Step 2
Solve the system of equations using substitution.

Isolate the y-variable in equation 1.
$$y - 12x = -69$$
$$y = 12x - 69$$

Step 3
Substitute the expression represented by the isolated variable from equation 1 into equation 2, and simplify.

Substitute $12x - 69$ for y in equation 2, and bring all terms to one side.
$$y - x^2 = -33$$
$$12x - 69 - x^2 = -33$$
$$0 = x^2 - 12x + 36$$

Step 4
Solve for x by factoring the quadratic equation.
$$0 = x^2 - 12x + 36$$
$$0 = (x-6)(x-6)$$
$$0 = (x-6)^2$$
$$0 = x - 6$$
$$x = 6$$

Step 5
Substitute the solved value of x into equation 1, and solve for y.
$$y - 12x = -69$$
$$y - 12(6) = -69$$
$$y - 72 = -69$$
$$y = 3$$

The two numbers are 6 and 3.

Classifying Systems of Equations

ANSWERS AND SOLUTIONS

1. **Step 1**
Subtract equation 2 from equation 1 to eliminate the y-variable.
$$① \quad 4x - 4 = x^2 - y$$
$$② \quad 5 = 2x - y$$
$$\overline{4x - 9 = x^2 - 2x}$$

Step 2
Solve for x.
$$4x - 9 = x^2 - 2x$$
$$0 = x^2 - 6x + 9$$
$$0 = (x-3)^2$$
$$0 = x - 3$$
$$3 = x$$

Step 3
Substitute the solved value of x into equation 2, and solve for y.
$$5 = 2x - y$$
$$5 = 2(3) - y$$
$$5 = 6 - y$$
$$y = 1$$

The system of equations has exactly one solution: $\{(3, 1)\}$.

Step 4
Verify the system of equations has one solution using a graphing calculator.

Rewrite equation 1 in the form $y = ax^2 + bx + c$ and equation 2 in the form $y = mx + b$.
$$4x - 4 = x^2 - y \qquad\qquad 5 = 2x - y$$
$$y = x^2 - 4x + 4 \qquad\qquad y = 2x - 5$$

Press $\boxed{Y=}$, and input each function.
$$Y_1 = x^2 - 4x + 4$$
$$Y_2 = 2x - 5$$

Press ZOOM , and select 6:ZStandard to obtain this window.

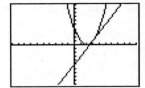

The graphs intersect at exactly one point. Press 2nd TRACE , and select 5:intersect. The graphs intersect at (3, 1).

2. **Step 1**
Isolate one variable from equation 1 or 2.

In this case, equation 1 has the y-variable isolated.

Step 2
Substitute the expression representing the isolated variable from equation 1 into equation 2, and simplify.

Substitute $x^2 + 3$ for y into equation 2, and bring all terms to one side.
$$x^2 = 5 - y$$
$$x^2 = 5 - \left(x^2 + 3\right)$$
$$x^2 = 5 - x^2 - 3$$
$$x^2 = -x^2 + 2$$
$$2x^2 - 2 = 0$$

Step 3
Solve for x.
$$2x^2 - 2 = 0$$
$$2x^2 = 2$$
$$x^2 = 1$$
$$x = \pm 1$$

Step 4
Substitute the solved values of x into equation 1, and solve for y.

$$y = x^2 + 3 \qquad y = x^2 + 3$$
$$y = (1)^2 + 3 \qquad y = (-1)^2 + 3$$
$$y = 4 \qquad\qquad y = 4$$

The system of equations has two solutions: $\{(1, 4), (-1, 4)\}$.

Step 5
Verify the system of equations has two solutions using a graphing calculator.

Rewrite equation 2 in the form $y = ax^2 + bx + c$.
$$x^2 = 5 - y$$
$$y = -x^2 + 5$$

Press Y = , and input each function.
$$Y_1 = x^2 + 3$$
$$Y_2 = -x^2 + 5$$

Press ZOOM , and select 6:ZStandard to obtain this window.

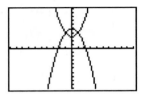

The graphs intersect at two points. Press 2nd TRACE , and select 5:intersect. The graphs intersect at (1, 4) and (–1, 4).

3. **Step 1**
Isolate one variable from equation 1 or 2.

In this case, equation 1 already has the y-variable isolated.

Step 2
Substitute the expression representing the isolated variable from equation 1 into equation 2, and simplify.

Substitute $(x - 3)^2$ for y in equation 2, and bring all terms to one side.
$$x^2 = y + 3$$
$$x^2 = (x - 3)^2 + 3$$
$$x^2 = x^2 - 6x + 9 + 3$$
$$0 = -6x + 12$$

Step 3
Solve for x.
$$0 = -6x + 12$$
$$6x = 12$$
$$x = 2$$

Step 4
Substitute the solved value of x into equation 1, and solve for y.
$$y = (x-3)^2$$
$$y = (2-3)^2$$
$$y = (-1)^2$$
$$y = 1$$

The system of equations has exactly one solution: $\{(2, 1)\}$.

Step 5
Verify the system of equations has one solution using a graphing calculator.

Rewrite equation 2 in the form $y = ax^2 + bx + c$.
$$x^2 = y + 3$$
$$x^2 - 3 = y$$

Press $\boxed{Y=}$, and input each function.
$$Y_1 = (x-3)^2$$
$$Y_2 = x^2 - 3$$

Press $\boxed{ZOOM}$, and select 6:ZStandard to obtain this window.

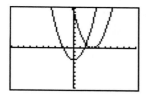

The graphs intersect at exactly one point.
Press $\boxed{2nd}$ $\boxed{TRACE}$, and select 5:intersect.
It can be found that the graphs intersect at $(2, 1)$.

4. Step 1
Isolate one variable from equation 1 or 2.

In this case, equation 1 has the y-variable isolated.

Step 2
Substitute the expression representing the isolated variable from equation 1 into equation 2, and simplify.

Substitute $7x^2 + 9x + 6$ for y in equation 2.
$$3(3x+2) = y - 7x^2$$
$$3(3x+2) = (7x^2 + 9x + 6) - 7x^2$$
$$9x + 6 = 9x + 6$$
$$0 = 0$$

Since $0 = 0$ is a true statement for every value of x, there are an infinite number of solutions for all values of x and y in this system of equations.

5. Step 1
Isolate one variable from equation 1 or 2.

In this case, equation 1 already has the y-variable isolated.

Step 2
Substitute the expression representing the isolated variable from equation 1 into equation 2, and simplify.

Substitute $-x + 4$ for y in equation 2, and bring all terms to one side.
$$y + 1 = -(x-3)^2$$
$$(-x+4) + 1 = -(x-3)^2$$
$$-x + 5 = -(x^2 - 6x + 9)$$
$$-x + 5 = -x^2 + 6x - 9$$
$$0 = -x^2 + 7x - 14$$

Step 3
Solve for x using the quadratic formula.
$$y = \frac{-b \pm \sqrt{b^2 - 4ac}}{2a}$$
$$y = \frac{-(7) \pm \sqrt{(7)^2 - 4(-1)(-14)}}{2(-1)}$$
$$y = \frac{-7 \pm \sqrt{49 - 56}}{-2}$$
$$y = \frac{7 \pm \sqrt{-7}}{2}$$

Since you cannot take the square root of a negative number, there is no solution.

Topic Practice Questions

ANSWERS AND SOLUTIONS

1. Step 1
Isolate one variable from equation 1 or 2.

In this case, equation 1 has the y-variable isolated.

Step 2
Substitute the expression represented by the isolated variable from equation 1 into equation 2, and simplify.

Substitute $x^2 - 9x$ for y in equation 2, and bring all terms to one side.

$$y + x = 9$$
$$\left(x^2 - 9x\right) + x = 9$$
$$x^2 - 9x + x = 9$$
$$x^2 - 8x = 9$$
$$x^2 - 8x - 9 = 0$$

Step 3
Solve for x by factoring the quadratic equation.

$$x^2 - 8x - 9 = 0$$
$$(x + 1)(x - 9) = 0$$

$x + 1 = 0$	$x - 9 = 0$
$x = -1$	$x = 9$

Step 4
Substitute the solved values of x into equation 2, and solve for y.

$y + x = 9$	$y + x = 9$
$y + (-1) = 9$	$y + 9 = 9$
$y - 1 = 9$	$y = 0$
$y = 10$	

The solution set is $\{(-1, 10), (9, 0)\}$.

Step 5
Graph the functions represented by the given equations using a graphing calculator.

Rewrite equation 2 in the form $y = mx + b$.

$$y + x = 9$$
$$y = -x + 9$$

Press $\boxed{Y =}$, and input each function.

$$Y_1 = x^2 - 9x$$
$$Y_2 = -x + 9$$

Press $\boxed{\text{GRAPH}}$. The window setting used to display the two graphs is $x : \left[-10, 15, 1\right]$ and $y : \left[-25, 15, 1\right]$.

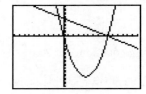

Step 6
Find the points of intersection.

Press $\boxed{\text{2nd}}\ \boxed{\text{TRACE}}$, and choose 5:intersect.

Determine the intersection point that is farthest to the left.

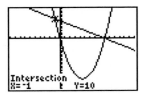

Repeat the process to find the intersection point that is farthest to the right.

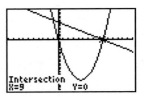

The calculator verifies that the points of intersection of the curve and the line are at $(-1, 10)$ and $(9, 0)$.

2. **Step 1**
Subtract equation 2 from equation 1 to eliminate the y-variable.

$$① \quad y - x^2 = 15x - 160$$
$$② \quad y - 33x = -2x^2 + 5$$
$$\overline{\quad -x^2 + 33x = 15x + 2x^2 - 165 \quad}$$

Step 2
Solve for x.

$$-x^2 + 33x = 15x + 2x^2 - 165$$
$$0 = 3x^2 - 18x - 165$$
$$0 = 3\left(x^2 - 6x - 55\right)$$
$$0 = 3(x - 11)(x + 5)$$
$$0 = (x - 11)(x + 5)$$

$x - 11 = 0$	$x + 5 = 0$
$x = 11$	$x = -5$

Step 3
Substitute the solved values of x into equation 1, and solve for y.

$$y - x^2 = 15x - 160$$
$$y - (11)^2 = 15(11) - 160$$
$$y - 121 = 165 - 160$$
$$y = 165 - 160 + 121$$
$$y = 126$$

$$y - x^2 = 15x - 160$$
$$y - (-5)^2 = 15(-5) - 160$$
$$y - 25 = -75 - 160$$
$$y = -75 - 160 + 25$$
$$y = -210$$

Therefore, the solution set is
$\{(11, 126), (-5, -210)\}$.

Step 4
Graph the functions represented by the given equations using a graphing calculator.

Rewrite equation 1 and equation 2 in the form $y = ax^2 + bx + c$.

$$y - x^2 = 15x - 160 \qquad y - 33x = -2x^2 + 5$$
$$y = x^2 + 15x - 160 \qquad y = -2x^2 + 33x + 5$$

Press $\boxed{Y =}$, and input each function.
$$Y_1 = x^2 + 15x - 160$$
$$Y_2 = -2x^2 + 33x + 5$$

Press $\boxed{\text{GRAPH}}$. The window setting used to display the two graphs is $x : [-50, 50, 5]$ and $y : [-240, 220, 20]$.

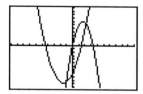

Step 5
Find the points of intersection.

Press $\boxed{\text{2nd}}$ $\boxed{\text{TRACE}}$, and choose 5:intersect.

Determine the intersection point that is farthest to the left.

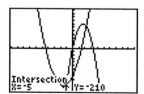

Repeat the process to find the intersection point that is farthest to the right.

The calculator verifies that the points of intersection of the two curves are at (11, 126) and (-5, -210).

3. **Step 1**
Multiply equation 1 by 2.
$$①×2 \quad 2(y = x^2 - x - 3) \rightarrow 2y = 2x^2 - 2x - 6$$

Let $2y = 2x^2 - 2x - 6$ represent equation 3.

Step 2
Subtract equation 3 from equation 2 to eliminate the y-variable.
$$② \quad 2y = 10x + 26$$
$$③ \quad \underline{2y = 2x^2 - 2x - 6}$$
$$0 = -2x^2 + 12x + 32$$

Step 3
Solve for x.
$$0 = -2x^2 + 12x + 32$$
$$0 = -2(x^2 - 6x - 16)$$
$$0 = -2(x - 8)(x + 2)$$
$$0 = (x - 8)(x + 2)$$
$$x - 8 = 0 \qquad x + 2 = 0$$
$$x = 8 \qquad x = -2$$

Step 4
Substitute the solved values for x into equation 2, and solve for y.
$$2y = 10x + 26 \qquad\qquad 2y = 10x + 26$$
$$2y = 10(8) + 26 \qquad\quad 2y = 10(-2) + 26$$
$$2y = 80 + 26 \qquad\qquad 2y = -20 + 26$$
$$2y = 106 \qquad\qquad\quad 2y = 6$$
$$y = 53 \qquad\qquad\qquad y = 3$$

The solution set is $\{(-2, 3), (8, 53)\}$.

Step 5
Graph the functions represented by the given equations using a graphing calculator.

Rewrite equation 2 in the form $y = mx + b$.
$$2y = 10x + 26$$
$$y = 5x + 13$$

Press $\boxed{Y=}$, and input each function.
$$Y_1 = x^2 - x - 3$$
$$Y_2 = 5x + 13$$

Press $\boxed{\text{GRAPH}}$. The window setting used to display the two graphs is $x : [-10, 10, 1]$ and $y : [-20, 80, 5]$.

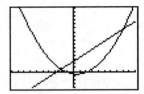

Step 6
Find the points of intersection.

Press $\boxed{\text{2nd}}$ $\boxed{\text{TRACE}}$, and choose 5:intersect. Determine the intersection point that is farthest to the left.

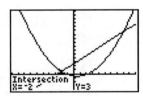

Repeat the process to find the intersection point that is farthest to the right.

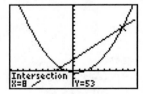

The calculator verifies that the points of intersection of the curve and the line are at $(-2, 3)$ and $(8, 53)$.

4. **Step 1**
Multiply equation 2 by 2.
$$②×2 \quad 2(8x - y = -3x^2 - 1) \rightarrow 16x - 2y = -6x^2 - 2$$

Let $16x - 2y = -6x^2 - 2$ represent equation 3.

Step 2
Subtract equation 3 from equation 1 to eliminate the y-variable.
$$① \quad 6x^2 - 2y = -16x - 2$$
$$③ \quad 16x - 2y = -6x^2 - 2$$
$$\overline{6x^2 - 16x = -16x + 6x^2}$$

Step 3
Solve for x.
$$6x^2 - 16x = -16x + 6x^2$$
$$0 = 0$$

Since $0 = 0$ is a true statement for every value of x, there are an infinite number of solutions for all values of x and y in this system of equations.

5. **Step 1**
Isolate one variable from equation 1 or 2. In this case, equation 1 already has the y-variable isolated.

Step 2
Substitute the expression represented by the isolated variable from equation 1 into equation 2, and simplify.

Substitute $25x + 47$ for y in equation 2, and bring all terms to one side.
$$y + 3x^2 = x - 1$$
$$(25x + 47) + 3x^2 = x - 1$$
$$3x^2 + 24x + 48 = 0$$

Step 3
Solve for x.
$$3x^2 + 24x + 48 = 0$$
$$3(x^2 + 8x + 16) = 0$$
$$3(x + 4)(x + 4) = 0$$
$$3(x + 4)^2 = 0$$
$$(x + 4)^2 = 0$$
$$x + 4 = 0$$
$$x = -4$$

Step 4
Substitute the solved value of x into equation 1, and solve for y.
$$y = 25x + 47$$
$$y = 25(-4) + 47$$
$$y = -100 + 47$$
$$y = -53$$

The system of equations has exactly one solution: $\{(-4, -53)\}$.

6. Step 1
Subtract equation 2 from equation 1 to eliminate the y-variable.

① $\quad y-17=3x^2+2x$
② $\quad y+2x^2=9$

$$-17-2x^2=3x^2+2x-9$$

Step 2
Solve for x.
$$-17-2x^2=3x^2+2x-9$$
$$0=5x^2+2x+8$$

Use the quadratic formula to solve the equation $0=5x^2+2x+8$.

$$y=\frac{-b\pm\sqrt{b^2-4ac}}{2a}$$
$$y=\frac{-(2)\pm\sqrt{(2)^2-4(5)(8)}}{2(5)}$$
$$y=\frac{-2\pm\sqrt{4-160}}{10}$$
$$y=\frac{-2\pm\sqrt{-156}}{10}$$

Since you cannot take the square root of a negative number, there is no solution.

7. The intersection points of the graphs of the functions correspond to the times at which the balls reach the same height.

Graph the equations using a graphing calculator.

Step 1
Press $\boxed{Y=}$, and input each function.
$$Y_1=-7.6(x-1.2)^2+15$$
$$Y_2=-21.1(x-0.8)^2+15$$

Press $\boxed{\text{GRAPH}}$. The window setting used to display the two graphs is $x:[0,3,1]$ and $y:[0,18,5]$.

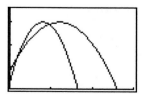

Step 2
Find the points of intersection.

Press $\boxed{\text{2nd}}$ $\boxed{\text{TRACE}}$, and choose 5:intersect.

Determine the intersection point that is farthest to the left.

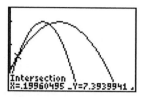

Repeat the process to find the intersection point that is farthest to the right.

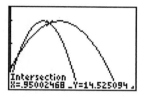

The first point of intersection is at approximately (0.20, 7.39), and the second point of intersection is at approximately (0.95, 14.53). The x-coordinate of each intersection point represents the time, t, and the y-coordinate represents the corresponding height, h.

Therefore, the balls reach the same height after 0.20 s and again after 0.95 s.

8. Step 1
Set up a system of equations.

If the car travelled 45 m after 1 s, then substitute 45 for D and 1 for t.
$$D=at^2+b^2t$$
$$45=a(1)^2+b^2(1)$$
$$45=a+b^2$$

If the car travelled 104 m after 2 s, then substitute 104 for D and 2 for t.
$$D=at^2+b^2t$$
$$104=a(2)^2+b^2(2)$$
$$104=4a+2b^2$$

Therefore, this is the system of equations:
① $\quad 45=a+b^2$
② $\quad 104=4a+2b^2$

Step 2
Solve the system of equations by elimination.

Multiply equation 1 by 2.
$$①×2 \quad 2\left(45 = a + b^2\right) → 90 = 2a + 2b^2$$

Let $90 = 2a + 2b^2$ represent equation 3.

Step 3
Subtract equation 2 from equation 3 to eliminate $2b^2$.
$$
\begin{array}{rl}
③ & 90 = 2a + 2b^2 \\
② & 104 = 4a + 2b^2 \\
\hline
& -14 = -2a
\end{array}
$$

Step 4
Solve for a.
$$-14 = -2a$$
$$7 = a$$

Step 5
Substitute the solved value of a into equation 1, and solve for b.
$$45 = a + b^2$$
$$45 = 7 + b^2$$
$$38 = b^2$$
$$b = \pm\sqrt{38}$$

Since b is positive, the value of a is 7 and the value of b is $\sqrt{38}$.

LINEAR AND QUADRATIC INEQUALITIES

Solving Quadratic Inequalities in One Variable Graphically

ANSWERS AND SOLUTIONS

1. **Step 1**
    Write the quadratic inequality in $ax^2 + bx + c < 0$ form.

    Rewrite with all the terms on the left side of the inequality.
    $$4x^2 < 2x$$
    $$4x^2 - 2x < 0$$

    Step 2
    Sketch the graph of the corresponding quadratic function.

    The quadratic function $f(x) = 4x^2 - 2x$ is a parabola that opens up.

    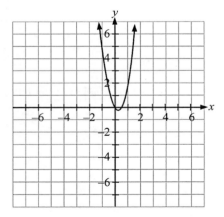

    Step 3
    Determine the boundary values.

    From the graph of the function, the x-intercepts are $(0, 0)$ and $(0.5, 0)$.

    Therefore, the boundary values are 0 and 0.5.

    Step 4
    Determine the solution to the inequality.

The solutions to the inequality $4x^2 < 2x$ will be the x-coordinates, where $f(x) < 0$ (below the x-axis), for the graph of $f(x) = 4x^2 - 2x$.

From the graph, the solution is $0 < x < 0.5$.

Step 5
Graph the solution on a number line.

Place the boundary values on the number line using open dots since these values are not included in the inequality.

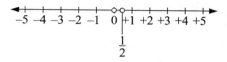

For the solution $0 < x < 0.5$, shade between the boundary values.

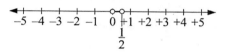

2. **Step 1**
Write the quadratic inequality in $ax^2 + bx + c \geq 0$ form.

Rewrite with all the terms on the left side of the inequality.
$$2x^2 + 5x \geq 12$$
$$2x^2 + 5x - 12 \geq 0$$

Step 2
Sketch the graph of the corresponding quadratic function.

The quadratic function $f(x) = 2x^2 + 5x - 12$ is a parabola that opens up.

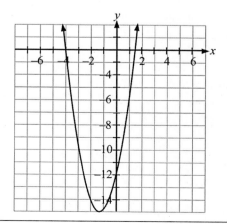

Step 3
Determine the boundary values.

From the graph of the function, the x-intercepts are $(-4, 0)$ and $(1.5, 0)$.

Therefore, the boundary values are -4 and 1.5.

Step 4
Determine the solution set to the inequality.

The solution to the inequality $2x^2 + 5x \geq 12$ will be the x-coordinates, where $f(x) \geq 0$ (above the x-axis and equal to zero), for the graph of $f(x) = 2x^2 + 5x - 12$.

From the graph, the solutions are $x \leq -4$ and $x \geq 1.5$.

Step 5
Graph the solution set on a number line.

Place the boundary values on the number line using solid dots since these values are included in the inequality.

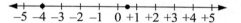

For the solution $x \leq -4$, shade to the left of the boundary value, and for the solution $x \geq 1.5$, shade to the right of the boundary value.

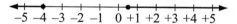

3. **Step 1**
Write the quadratic inequality in $ax^2 + bx + c < 0$ form.

Rewrite with all the terms on the left side of the inequality.
$$6x^2 < 15x + 9$$
$$6x^2 - 15x - 9 < 0$$

Step 2
Sketch the graph of the corresponding quadratic function.

The quadratic function $f(x) = 6x^2 - 15x - 9$ is a parabola that opens up.

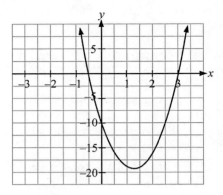

Step 3
Determine the boundary values.

From the graph of the function, the x-intercepts are $\left(-\dfrac{1}{2}, 0\right)$ and $(3, 0)$.

Therefore, the boundary values are $-\dfrac{1}{2}$ and 3.

Step 4
Determine the solution set to the inequality.

The solution to the inequality $6x^2 < 15x + 9$ will be the x-coordinates, where $f(x) < 0$ (below the x-axis), for the graph of $f(x) = 6x^2 - 15x - 9$.

From the graph, the solution is $-\dfrac{1}{2} < x < 3$.

Step 5
Graph the solution set on a number line.

Place the boundary values on a number line using open dots since these values are not included in the inequality.

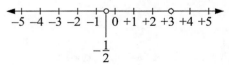

For the solution $-\dfrac{1}{2} < x < 3$, shade between the boundary values.

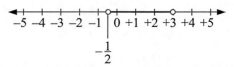

4. **Step 1**
Graph the function using a graphing calculator.

Press $\boxed{Y=}$, and enter the function as $Y_1 = 2x^2 + 9x - 5$.

Press $\boxed{WINDOW}$, and enter a window setting of $x:[-10, 10, 1]$ and $y:[-15, 10, 1]$.

Press $\boxed{GRAPH}$ to obtain this screen.

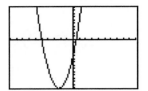

Step 2
Determine the x-intercepts of the graph.

Press $\boxed{2nd}$ $\boxed{TRACE}$, and select 2:zero. Move the cursor to the left of the first x-intercept, and press $\boxed{ENTER}$. Next, move the cursor to the right of the same x-intercept, and press $\boxed{ENTER}$ twice. Repeat to find the other x-intercept.

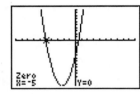 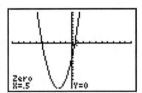

The x-intercepts are $x = -5$ and $x = 0.5$.

Step 3
Determine the solution set to the inequality $2x^2 + 9x - 5 \leq 0$.

The solution to the inequality $2x^2 + 9x - 5 \leq 0$ will be the x-coordinates, where $f(x) \leq 0$ (below the x-axis and zero), for the graph of $f(x) = 2x^2 + 9x - 5$.

From the graph, the solution, to the nearest tenth, is approximately $-5.0 \leq x \leq 0.5$.

5. **Step 1**
Write the quadratic inequality in
$ax^2 + bx + c > 0$ form.

Eliminate the denominator by multiplying both sides of the inequality by 2, and rewrite with all the terms on the left side of the inequality.

$$2x - 3 > -\frac{5}{2}x^2$$
$$4x - 6 > -5x^2$$
$$5x^2 + 4x - 6 > 0$$

Step 2
Graph the function $f(x) = 5x^2 + 4x - 6$ using a graphing calculator.

Press $\boxed{Y=}$, and enter the function as
$Y_1 = 5x^2 + 4x - 6$.

Press $\boxed{ZOOM}$, and select 6:ZStandard to obtain this screen.

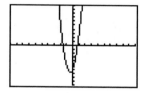

Step 3
Determine the x-intercepts of the graph.

Press $\boxed{2nd}$ $\boxed{CALC}$, and select 2:zero. Move the cursor to the left of the first x-intercept, and press $\boxed{ENTER}$. Next, move the cursor to the right of the same x-intercept, and press $\boxed{ENTER}$ twice. Repeat to find the other x-intercept.

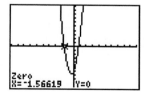 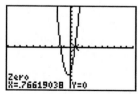

To the nearest tenth, the x-intercepts are $x \doteq -1.6$ and $x \doteq 0.8$.

Step 4
Determine the solution set to the inequality.

The solution to the inequality $2x - 3 > -\frac{5}{2}x^2$ will be the x-coordinates, where $f(x) > 0$ (above the x-axis), for the graph of $f(x) = 5x^2 + 4x - 6$.

From the graph, the solutions are approximately $x < -1.6$ and $x > 0.8$.

6. **Step 1**
Write the quadratic inequality in
$ax^2 + bx + c \leq 0$ form.

Rewrite with all the terms on the left side of the inequality.
$$-7x^2 \leq 3x - 8$$
$$-7x^2 - 3x + 8 \leq 0$$

Step 2
Graph the function using a graphing calculator.

Press $\boxed{Y=}$, and enter the function as
$Y_1 = -7x^2 - 3x + 8$.

Press $\boxed{ZOOM}$, and select 6:ZStandard to obtain this window.

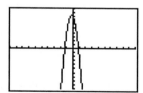

Step 3
Determine the x-intercepts of the graph.

Press $\boxed{2nd}$ $\boxed{CALC}$, and select 2:zero. Move the cursor to the left of the first x-intercept, and press $\boxed{ENTER}$. Next, move the cursor to the right of the same x-intercept, and press $\boxed{ENTER}$ twice. Repeat to find the other x-intercept.

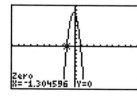 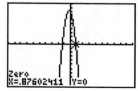

To the nearest tenth, the x-intercepts are $x \doteq -1.3$ and $x \doteq 0.9$.

Step 4
Determine the solution set to the inequality.

The solution set to the inequality $-7x^2 \le 3x - 8$ will be the x-coordinates, where $f(x) \le 0$ (below the x-axis and equal to zero), for the graph of $f(x) = -7x^2 - 3x + 8$.

From the graph, the solutions are approximately $x \le -1.3$ and $x \ge 0.9$.

7. **Step 1**
Model the given information with an inequality.

Since the profit must be at least \$1 450, an inequality statement that represents the information in the given problem is $-6x^2 + 240x - 350 \ge 1450$.

Step 2
Write the quadratic inequality in $ax^2 + bx + c > 0$ form.

Subtract 1 450 from each side of the inequality $-6x^2 + 240x - 350 \ge 1450$.

$$-6x^2 + 240x - 350 \ge 1450$$
$$-6x^2 + 240x - 350 - 1450 \ge 0$$
$$-6x^2 + 240x - 1800 \ge 0$$

Step 3
Graph the function using a graphing calculator.

Press $\boxed{Y=}$, and enter the function as $Y_1 = -6x^2 + 240x - 1800$.

Press $\boxed{\text{WINDOW}}$, and enter a window setting of $x:[-10, 50, 10]$ and $y:[-2500, 1000, 200]$.

Press $\boxed{\text{GRAPH}}$ to obtain this screen.

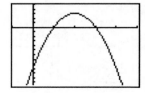

Step 4
Determine the x-intercepts of the graph.

Press $\boxed{\text{2nd}}$ $\boxed{\text{CALC}}$, and select 2:zero. Move the cursor to the left of the first x-intercept, and press $\boxed{\text{ENTER}}$. Next, move the cursor to the right of the same x-intercept, and press $\boxed{\text{ENTER}}$ twice. Repeat to find the other x-intercept.

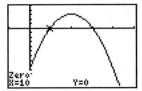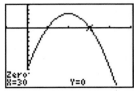

The x-intercepts of the function are 10 and 30.

Step 5
Determine the solution set to the inequality.

The solution set to the inequality $-6x^2 + 240x - 350 \ge 1450$ will be the x-coordinates, where $f(x) \ge 0$ (above the x-axis and zero), for the graph of $f(x) = -6x^2 + 240x - 1800$.

In order for Naya to make a profit of at least \$1 450, the selling price per necklace must be between \$10 and \$30 inclusive.

Solving Quadratic Inequalities in One Variable without a Graph

ANSWERS AND SOLUTIONS

1. **Step 1**
Factor the quadratic inequality.
$$3x^2 - 2x - 8 \le 0$$
$$(3x + 4)(x - 2) \le 0$$

Step 2
Determine the boundary values.
$$3x + 4 = 0 \qquad\qquad x - 2 = 0$$
$$3x = -4 \qquad\qquad\quad x = 2$$
$$x = -\frac{4}{3}$$

The boundary values are $x = -\frac{4}{3}$ and $x = 2$.

Step 3
Place the boundary values on a number line, and identify the possible solution regions.

Solid dots are used because $x = -\dfrac{4}{3}$ and $x = 2$ are included in the inequality.

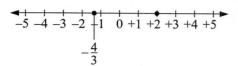

$$-\frac{4}{3}$$

There are three regions on the number line:
$x < -\dfrac{4}{3}$, $-\dfrac{4}{3} < x < 2$, and $x > 2$.

Step 4
Use test points to determine the solution regions on the number line that satisfy the inequality.

Possible test points for the inequality $(3x+4)(x-2) \le 0$ are -2, 0, and 3.

Region	Test Point	$(3x+4)(x-2)$	Sign
$x < -\dfrac{4}{3}$	-2	$\begin{aligned}&(3(-2)+4)(-2-2)\\&=(-2)(-4)\\&=8\end{aligned}$	$+$
$-\dfrac{4}{3} < x < 2$	0	$\begin{aligned}&(3(0)+4)(0-2)\\&=(4)(-2)\\&=-8\end{aligned}$	$-$
$x > 2$	3	$\begin{aligned}&(3(3)+4)(3-2)\\&=(13)(1)\\&=13\end{aligned}$	$+$

Step 5
Identify the solution region.

Since $3x^2 - 2x - 8 \le 0$ is required, the solution consists of the values in the regions where the product is negative or zero. Thus, the solution is $-\dfrac{4}{3} \le x \le 2$.

Step 6
Graph the solution on the number line.

$$-\frac{4}{3}$$

2. Step 1
Factor the quadratic inequality.
$$-x + 6 < 2x^2$$
$$-2x^2 - x + 6 < 0$$
$$-\left(2x^2 + x - 6\right) < 0$$
$$-(2x-3)(x+2) < 0$$
$$(2x-3)(x+2) > 0$$

Step 2
Determine the boundary values.
$$2x - 3 = 0$$
$$2x = 3$$
$$x = \frac{3}{2}$$

$$x + 2 = 0$$
$$x = -2$$

The boundary values are $x = -2$ and $x = \dfrac{3}{2}$.

Step 3
Place the boundary values on a number line, and identify the possible solution regions.

Open dots are used because $x = -2$ and $x = \dfrac{3}{2}$ are not included in the inequality.

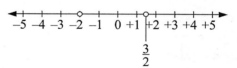

$$\frac{3}{2}$$

There are three regions on the number line:
$x < -2$, $-2 < x < \dfrac{3}{2}$, and $x > \dfrac{3}{2}$.

Step 4
Use test points to determine the solution regions on the number line that satisfy the inequality.

Possible test points for the inequality $(2x-3)(x+2) > 0$ are -3, 0, and 2.

Region	Test Point	$(2x-1)(x+2)$	Sign
$x < -2$	-3	$\begin{aligned}(2(-3)-3)(-3+2)\\=(-9)(-1)\\=9\end{aligned}$	+
$-2 < x < \dfrac{3}{2}$	0	$\begin{aligned}(2(0)-3)(0+2)\\=(-3)(2)\\=-6\end{aligned}$	−
$x > \dfrac{3}{2}$	2	$\begin{aligned}(2(2)-3)(2+2)\\=(1)(4)\\=4\end{aligned}$	+

Step 5
Identify the solution region.

Since $(2x-3)(x+2) > 0$ is required, the solution consists of the values in the regions where the product is positive. Thus, the solutions are $x < -2$ and $x > \dfrac{3}{2}$.

Step 6
Graph the solutions on the number line.

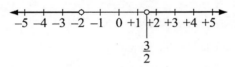

3. Step 1
Factor the quadratic inequality.
$$x^2 + x - 12 > 18$$
$$x^2 + x - 30 > 0$$
$$(x+6)(x-5) > 0$$

Step 2
Determine the boundary values.

$x + 6 = 0$	$x - 5 = 0$
$x = -6$	$x = 5$

The boundary values are $x = -6$ and $x = 5$.

Step 3
Place the boundary values on a number line, and identify the possible solution regions.

Open dots are used because $x = -6$ and $x = 5$ are not included in the inequality.

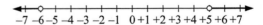

There are three regions on the number line:
$x < -6$, $-6 < x < 5$, and $x > 5$.

Step 4
Use test points to determine the solution regions on the number line that satisfy the inequality.

Possible test points for the inequality $(x+6)(x-5) > 0$ are -7, 0, and 6.

Region	Test Point	$(x+6)(x-5)$	Sign
$x < -6$	-7	$\begin{aligned}(-7+6)(-7-5)\\=(-1)(-12)\\=12\end{aligned}$	+
$-6 < x < 5$	0	$\begin{aligned}(0+6)(0-5)\\=(6)(-5)\\=-30\end{aligned}$	−
$x > 5$	6	$\begin{aligned}(6+6)(6-5)\\=(12)(1)\\=12\end{aligned}$	+

Step 5
Identify the solution region.

Since $(x+6)(x-5) > 0$ is required, the solution consists of the values in the regions where the product is positive. Thus, the solutions are $x < -6$ and $x > 5$.

Step 6
Graph the solutions on the number line.

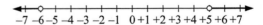

4. Step 1
Factor the quadratic inequality.
$$x^2 \geq -11x - 24$$
$$x^2 + 11x + 24 \geq 0$$
$$(x+3)(x+8) \geq 0$$

Step 2
Determine the boundary values.

$x + 3 = 0$	$x + 8 = 0$
$x = -3$	$x = -8$

The boundary values are $x = -8$ and $x = -3$.

Step 3
Place the boundary values on a number line, and identify the possible solution regions.

Solid dots are used because $x = -8$ and $x = -3$ are included in the inequality.

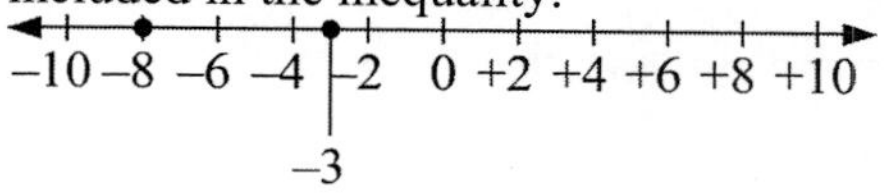

There are three regions on the number line: $x < -8$, $-8 < x < -3$, and $x > -3$.

Step 4
Use test points to determine the solution regions on the number line that satisfy the inequality.

Possible test points for the inequality $(x+3)(x+8) \geq 0$ are −10, −5, and 0.

Region	**Test Point**	$(x+3)(x+8)$	**Sign**
$x < -8$	−10	$(-10+3)(-10+8)$ $=(-7)(-2)$ $=14$	+
$-8 < x < -3$	−5	$(-5+3)(-5+8)$ $=(-2)(3)$ $=-6$	−
$x > -3$	0	$(0+3)(0+8)$ $=(3)(8)$ $=24$	+

Step 5
Identify the solution region.

Since $(x+3)(x+8) \geq 0$ is required, the solution consists of the values in the regions where the product is positive or zero. Thus, the solutions are $x \leq -8$ and $x \geq -3$.

Step 6
Graph the solutions on the number line.

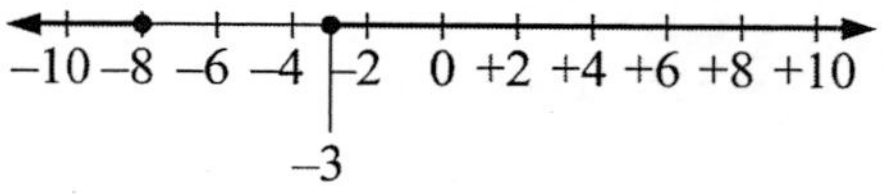

5. Step 1
Factor the quadratic inequality.

$$-\frac{1}{3}x^2 - \frac{2}{3}x > -5$$
$$-\frac{1}{3}x^2 - \frac{2}{3}x + 5 > 0$$
$$-x^2 - 2x + 15 > 0$$
$$-\left(x^2 + 2x - 15\right) > 0$$
$$-(x-3)(x+5) > 0$$
$$(x-3)(x+5) < 0$$

Step 2
Determine the boundary values.

$x - 3 = 0$ $\qquad$ $x + 5 = 0$
$x = 3$ $\qquad$ $x = -5$

The boundary values are $x = -5$ and $x = 3$.

Step 3
Place the boundary values on a number line, and identify the possible solution regions.

Open dots are used because $x = -5$ and $x = 3$ are not included in the inequality.

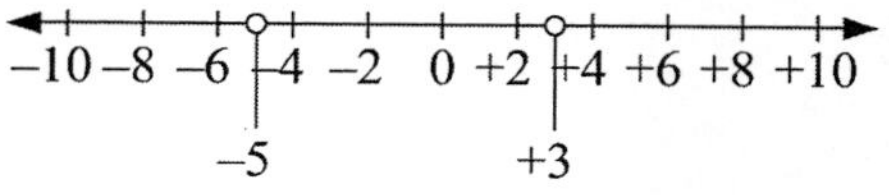

There are three regions on the number line: $x < -5$, $-5 < x < 3$, and $x > 3$.

Step 4
Use test points to determine the solution regions on the number line that satisfy the inequality.
Possible test points for the inequality $(x-3)(x+5) < 0$ are −10, 0, and 5.

Region	**Test Point**	$(x-3)(x+5)$	**Sign**
$x < -5$	−10	$(-10-3)(-10+5)$ $=(-13)(-5)$ $=65$	+
$-5 < x < 3$	0	$(0-3)(0+5)$ $=(-3)(5)$ $=-15$	−
$x > 3$	5	$(5-3)(5+5)$ $=(2)(10)$ $=20$	+

Step 5
Identify the solution region.

Since $(x-3)(x+5) < 0$ is required, the solution consists of the values in the regions where the product is negative. Thus, the solution is $-5 < x < 3$.

Step 6
Graph the solution on the number line.

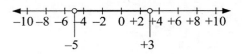

6. **Step 1**
Determine the inequality that represents the problem.

Let x and $x + 2$ represent the integers that differ by 2.

Since the product of the integers is less than 15, the inequality is $x(x+2) < 15$.

Step 2
Factor the quadratic inequality.
$$x(x+2) < 15$$
$$x^2 + 2x < 15$$
$$x^2 + 2x < 15$$
$$x^2 + 2x - 15 < 0$$
$$(x+5)(x-3) < 0$$

Step 3
Determine the boundary values.
$$x + 5 = 0 \qquad x - 3 = 0$$
$$x = -5 \qquad x = 3$$

The boundary values are $x = -5$ and $x = 3$.

Step 4
Use test points to determine the solution regions that satisfy the inequality.

There are three regions: $x < -5$, $-5 < x < 3$, and $x > 3$.

Possible test points for the inequality $(x+5)(x-3) < 0$ are -10, 0, and 10.

Region	Test Point	$(x+5)(x-3)$	Sign
$x < -5$	-10	$((-10)+5)(-10-3)$ $=(-5)(-13)$ $=65$	+
$-5 < x < 3$	0	$(0+5)(0-3)$ $=(5)(-3)$ $=-15$	−
$x > 3$	10	$(10+5)(10-3)$ $=(15)(7)$ $=105$	+

Step 5
Identify the solution region.

Since $(x+5)(x-3) < 0$ is required, the solution consists of the values in the regions where the product is negative. Thus, the solution is $-5 < x < 3$.

Step 6
Determine the possible pairs of integers.

Since the solution for x is any integer between -5 and 3, x can be -4, -3, -2, -1, 0, 1, and 2.

The possible pairs of integers represented by x and $x + 2$ are shown in this chart.

x	$x + 2$
-4	-2
-3	-1
-2	0
-1	1
0	2
1	3
2	4

Note that the product of each pair is less than 15.

Linear and Quadratic Inequalities in Two Variables

ANSWERS AND SOLUTIONS

1. **Step 1**
Isolate the y-variable.

The y-variable is already isolated.

Step 2
Determine whether the boundary line will be dotted or solid.

Since the inequality is $\leq$, the boundary line is part of the solution set.

The boundary line will be solid.

Step 3
Graph the corresponding linear equation that represents the inequality with the appropriate line.

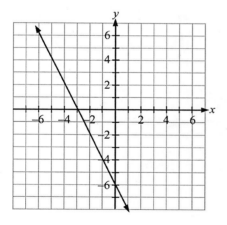

Step 4
Determine which side of the boundary line is to be shaded.

Substitute the test point (0, 0) into the inequality $y \leq -2x - 6$.
$$y \leq -2x - 6$$
$$0 \leq -2(0) - 6$$
$$0 \leq 0 - 6$$
$$0 \leq -6$$

The point (0, 0) does not satisfy the inequality, so the side that includes (0, 0) should not be shaded.

Step 5
Shade the appropriate side of the boundary line.

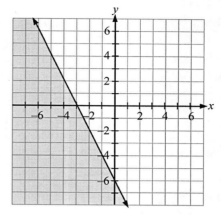

The solution set to the inequality $y \leq -2x - 6$ is the shaded region of the graph.

2. **Step 1**
Isolate the y-variable.
$$3x - 4y - 8 < 0$$
$$-4y < -3x + 8$$
$$y > \frac{3}{4}x - 2$$

Step 2
Determine whether the boundary line will be dotted or solid.

Since the inequality is >, the boundary line is not part of the solution set.

The boundary line will be dotted.

Step 3
Graph the corresponding linear equation that represents the inequality with the appropriate line.

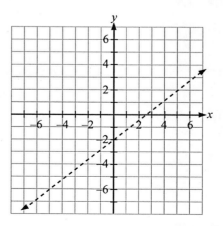

Step 4
Determine which side of the boundary line is to be shaded.

Substitute the test point (0, 0) into the inequality $3x - 4y - 8 < 0$.

$$3x - 4y - 8 < 0$$
$$3(0) - 4(0) - 8 < 0$$
$$0 - 0 - 8 < 0$$
$$-8 < 0$$

The point (0, 0) satisfies the inequality, so the side that includes (0, 0) should be shaded.

Step 5
Shade the appropriate side of the boundary line.

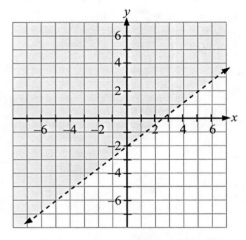

The solution set to the inequality $3x - 4y - 8 < 0$ is the shaded region of the graph.

3. **Step 1**
Isolate the y-variable.

$$-\frac{y}{2} > x^2 - 2x$$
$$-y > 2x^2 - 4x$$
$$y < -2x^2 + 4x$$

Step 2
Determine whether the boundary line will be dotted or solid.

Since the inequality is <, the boundary line is not part of the solution set.

The boundary line will be dotted.

Step 3
Graph the corresponding quadratic equation that represents the inequality with the appropriate line.

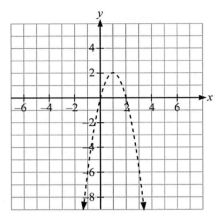

Step 4
Determine which side of the boundary line is to be shaded.

Substitute the test point (1, 1) into the inequality $-\frac{y}{2} > x^2 - 2x$.

$$-\frac{y}{2} > x^2 - 2x$$
$$-\frac{1}{2} > (1)^2 - 2(1)$$
$$-\frac{1}{2} > 1 - 2$$
$$-\frac{1}{2} > -1$$

The point (1, 1) satisfies the inequality, so the side that includes (1, 1) should be shaded.

Step 5
Shade the appropriate side of the boundary line.

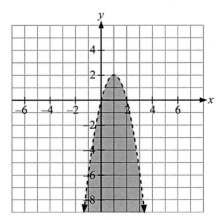

The solution set to the inequality $-\dfrac{y}{2} > x^2 - 2x$ is the shaded region of the graph.

4. **Step 1**
Isolate the y-variable.
$$-y - 3 \geq -x^2 - 2x$$
$$-y \geq -x^2 - 2x + 3$$
$$y \leq x^2 + 2x - 3$$

Step 2
Determine whether the boundary line will be dotted or solid.

Since the inequality is $\leq$, the boundary line is part of the solution set.

The boundary line will be solid.

Step 3
Graph the corresponding quadratic equation that represents the inequality with the appropriate line.

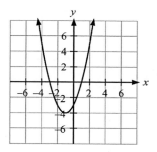

Step 4
Determine which side of the boundary line is to be shaded.

Substitute the test point $(0, 0)$ into the inequality $-y - 3 \geq -x^2 - 2x$.

$$-y - 3 \geq -x^2 - 2x$$
$$-(0) - 3 \geq -(0)^2 - 2(0)$$
$$0 - 3 \geq 0 - 0$$
$$-3 \geq 0$$

The point $(0, 0)$ does not satisfy the inequality, so the side that includes $(0, 0)$ should not be shaded.

Step 5
Shade the appropriate side of the boundary line.

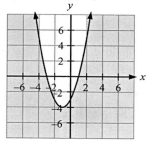

The solution set to the inequality $-y - 3 \geq -x^2 - 2x$ is the shaded region of the graph.

5. **Step 1**
Determine the equation of the boundary line using points on the line.

The points at $(0, 10)$ and $(1, 5)$ lie on the boundary line.

Use the slope formula to determine the slope, m, of the line.
$$m = \left(\frac{y_2 - y_1}{x_2 - x_1}\right)$$
$$m = \left(\frac{5 - 10}{1 - 0}\right)$$
$$m = \frac{-5}{1}$$
$$m = -5$$
Since the y-intercept from the graph is 10, the equation of the boundary line is $y = -5x + 10$.

Step 2
Determine the inequality sign.

Since the boundary line is solid, the inequality sign is $\leq$ or $\geq$.

Remove the equal sign in the equation $y = -5x + 10$. Using a point from the shaded region, such as $(2, 5)$, evaluate both sides to determine the appropriate inequality sign.
$$y \,\square\, -5x + 10$$
$$5 \,\square\, -5(2) + 10$$
$$5 \,\square\, -10 + 10$$
$$5 \,\square\, 0$$

Since 5 is greater than 0, the correct sign is $\geq$.

Therefore, the inequality is $y \geq -5x + 10$.

Not for Reproduction — 169 — Math 20-1 Problem Solved

6. **Step 1**

Determine the equation of the boundary line using points on the line.

From the vertex, the values of p and q are 0 and –2, respectively. A point on the parabola is (2, 2), so $x = 2$ and $y = 2$.

Substituting the known values into the equation $y = a(x - p) + q$, find the value of a.

$$y = a(x - p)^2 + q$$
$$2 = a(2 - 0)^2 + (-2)$$
$$2 = a(2)^2 - 2$$
$$4 = 4a$$
$$a = 1$$

The equation of the boundary line is $y = x^2 - 2$.

Step 2

Determine the inequality sign.

Since the boundary line is solid, the inequality sign is $\leq$ or $\geq$.

Remove the equal sign in the equation $y = x^2 - 2$. Using a point from the shaded region, such as (1, –4), evaluate both sides to determine the appropriate inequality sign.

$$y \ \square \ x^2 - 2$$
$$-4 \ \square \ (1)^2 - 2$$
$$-4 \ \square \ 1 - 2$$
$$-4 \ \square \ -1$$

Since –4 is less than –1, the correct sign is $\leq$.

Therefore, the inequality is $y \leq x^2 - 2$.

7. **Step1**

Isolate the y-variable.

$$\frac{9}{2}x - 8y \geq 6$$
$$-8y \geq -\frac{9}{2}x + 6$$
$$y \leq \frac{9}{16}x - \frac{3}{4}$$

Step 2

Press $\boxed{Y=}$, and enter the equation of the boundary line.

$$Y_1 = \frac{9}{16}x - \frac{3}{4}$$

Step 3

Determine which side of the boundary line is to be shaded.

Move the cursor to the left of $Y_1 = \frac{9}{16}x - \frac{3}{4}$, where the dotted line flashes. Since the inequality symbol used is $\leq$, press $\boxed{ENTER}$ three times or until the image ◣ appears.

Step 4

Press $\boxed{ZOOM}$, and select 6:ZStandard to obtain this screen.

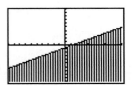

The graph of the solution of $\frac{9}{2}x - 8 \geq 6$ is displayed.

8. **Step 1**

Isolate the y-variable.

$$\frac{5}{4}x^2 - 1 > -\frac{1}{4}y - \frac{11}{4}x$$
$$5x^2 - 4 > -y - 11x$$
$$y > -5x^2 - 11x + 4$$

Step 2

Press $\boxed{Y=}$, and enter the equation of the boundary line.

$$Y_1 = -5x^2 - 11x + 4$$

Step 3

Determine which side of the boundary line is to be shaded.

Move the cursor to the left of $Y_1 = -5x^2 - 11x + 4$, where the dotted line flashes. Since the inequality symbol used is >, press $\boxed{ENTER}$ twice or until the image ◤ appears.

Step 4
Press ZOOM , and select 6:ZStandard to obtain this screen.

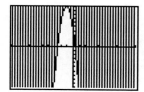

The graph of the solution of $\frac{5}{4}x^2 - 1 > -\frac{1}{4}y - \frac{11}{4}x$ is displayed.

9. If the amount of money that Fred contributes is represented by x and the amount of money Andy contributes is represented by y, then the amount of money they contribute together can be represented by the inequality $x + y \leq 500$.

10. The inequality that must be represented is $x + y \leq 500$. The solution consists of all ordered pairs on the line $x + y = 500$, as well as ordered pairs that lie in the region bounded by $x + y = 500$, the x-axis, and the y-axis.

Solutions are limited to positive values with two decimal places (dollars and cents).

The ordered pairs represent amounts of money that could be contributed by Fred (x-values) and Andy (y-values).

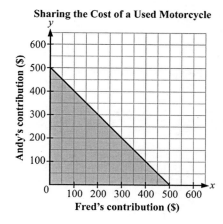

Sharing the Cost of a Used Motorcycle

Topic Practice Questions

ANSWERS AND SOLUTIONS

1. The solution to the inequality $f(x) \leq 0$ consists of the x-coordinates, where $f(x) \leq 0$ (below the x-axis and zero), for the graph of $f(x)$. The graph shows that the solutions are the values of x that are between -2 and 6. Therefore, the solution is $-2 \leq x \leq 6$.

2. **Step 1**
Factor the quadratic inequality.
$$-x^2 \leq 5x - 36$$
$$-x^2 - 5x + 36 \leq 0$$
$$-(x^2 + 5x - 36) \leq 0$$
$$-(x + 9)(x - 4) \leq 0$$
$$(x + 9)(x - 4) \geq 0$$

Step 2
Determine the boundary values.
$$x + 9 = 0 \qquad\qquad x - 4 = 0$$
$$x = -9 \qquad\qquad\qquad x = 4$$

The boundary values are $x = -9$ and $x = 4$.

Step 3
Place the boundary values on a number line, and identify the possible solution regions.

Solid dots are used because $x = -9$ and $x = 4$ are included in the inequality.

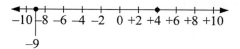

There are three regions on the number line: $x < -9$, $-9 < x < 4$, and $x > 4$.

Step 4
Use test points to determine the sign of the expression $(x + 9)(x - 4)$ in each of the three regions.

Possible test points are -10, 0, and 10.

Region	Test Point	$(x+9)(x-4)$	Sign
$x < -9$	-10	$\begin{aligned} &((-10)+9)(-10-4) \\ &= (-1)(-14) \\ &= 14 \end{aligned}$	$+$
$-9 < x < 4$	0	$\begin{aligned} &(0+9)(0-4) \\ &= (9)(-4) \\ &= -36 \end{aligned}$	$-$
$x > 4$	10	$\begin{aligned} &(10+9)(10-4) \\ &= (19)(6) \\ &= 114 \end{aligned}$	$+$

Step 5
Identify the solution region.

Since $(x+9)(x-4) \geq 0$ is required, the solution consists of the values in the regions where the product is positive and zero. Thus, the solutions are $x \leq -9$ and $x \geq 4$.

Step 6
Graph the solution set on the number line.

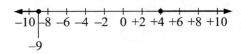

3. **Step 1**
Isolate the y-variable.
$$\frac{3x-52}{2} \geq 2y - 16$$
$$3x - 52 \geq 4y - 32$$
$$-4y \geq -3x + 52 - 32$$
$$-4y \geq -3x + 20$$
$$y \leq \frac{3}{4}x - 5$$

Step 2
Determine whether the boundary line will be dotted or solid.

Since the inequality is $\leq$, the boundary line is part of the solution set.

The boundary line will be solid.

Step 3
Graph the corresponding linear equation that represents the inequality, with the appropriate line.

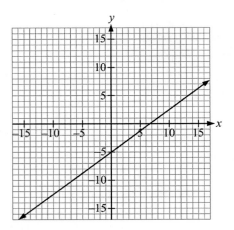

Step 4
Determine which side of the boundary line is to be shaded.

Substitute the test point $(0, 0)$ into the inequality $\frac{3x-52}{2} \geq 2y - 16$.
$$\frac{3x-52}{2} \geq 2y - 16$$
$$\frac{3(0)-52}{2} \geq 2(0) - 16$$
$$\frac{0-52}{2} \geq 0 - 16$$
$$-26 \geq -16$$

The point $(0, 0)$ does not satisfy the inequality, so the side that includes $(0, 0)$ should not be shaded.

Step 5
Shade the appropriate side of the boundary line.

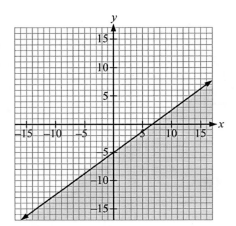

The solution set to the inequality $\dfrac{3x-52}{2} \geq 2y-16$ is the shaded region of the graph.

4.   Step 1
Determine the equation of the boundary line using points on the line.

The points at (0, 2) and (1, 0) lie on the boundary line.

Use the slope formula to determine the slope, m, of the line.

$$m = \left(\frac{y_2 - y_1}{x_2 - x_1}\right)$$
$$m = \left(\frac{0-2}{1-0}\right)$$
$$m = \left(\frac{-2}{1}\right)$$
$$m = -2$$

Since the y-intercept is 2 from the graph, the equation of the boundary line is $y = -2x+2$.

Step 2
Determine the inequality sign.

Since the boundary line is solid, the inequality sign is $\leq$ or $\geq$.

Remove the equal sign in the equation $y = -2x+2$. Using a point from the shaded region, such as (0, 0), evaluate both sides to determine the appropriate inequality sign.

$$y \ \square\ -2x+2$$
$$0 \ \square\ -2(0)+2$$
$$0 \ \square\ 0+2$$
$$0 \ \square\ 2$$

Since 0 is less than 2, the correct inequality sign is $\leq$.

Therefore, the inequality is $y \leq -2x+2$.

5.   Step 1
Isolate the y-variable.
$$x^2 - 9x \leq y + x$$
$$-y \leq -x^2 + 9x + x$$
$$-y \leq -x^2 + 10x$$
$$y \geq x^2 - 10x$$

Step 2
Determine whether the boundary line will be dotted or solid.

Since the inequality is $\geq$, the boundary line is part of the solution set.

The boundary line will be solid.

Step 3
Graph the corresponding quadratic equation that represents the inequality with the appropriate line.

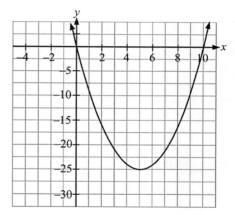

Step 4
Determine which side of the boundary line is to be shaded.

Substitute the test point (1, 1) into the inequality $x^2 - 9x \leq y + x$.
$$x^2 - 9x \leq y + x$$
$$(1)^2 - 9(1) \leq 1 + 1$$
$$-8 \leq 2$$

The point (1, 1) satisfies the inequality, so the side that includes (1, 1) should be shaded.

Step 5
Shade the appropriate side of the boundary line.

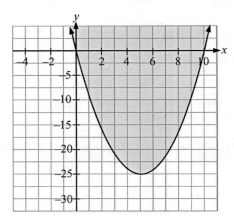

The solution set to the inequality $x^2 - 9x \le y + x$ is the shaded region of the graph.

6. **Step 1**
    Model the given information with an inequality.

    Since the stone must be less than 39.2 m above the river, an inequality statement that represents the problem is $24.5 + 19.6t - 4.9t^2 < 39.2$.

    Step 2
    Write the quadratic inequality in $ax^2 + bx + c < 0$ form.

    Subtract 39.2 from each side of the inequality $24.5 + 19.6t - 4.9t^2 < 39.2$.
    $$24.5 + 19.6t - 4.9t^2 < 39.2$$
    $$24.5 - 39.2 + 19.6t - 4.9t^2 < 0$$
    $$-14.7 + 19.6t - 4.9t^2 < 0$$

    Step 3
    Graph the function using a graphing calculator.

    Press $\boxed{Y=}$, and enter the function as $Y_1 = -14.7 + 19.6x - 4.9x^2$.

    Press $\boxed{ZOOM}$, and select 6:ZStandard to obtain this screen shot.

    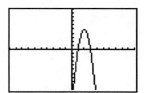

Step 4
Determine the t-intercepts of the function.

Press $\boxed{2nd}$ $\boxed{TRACE}$, and select 2:zero. Move the cursor to the left of the first x-intercept, and press $\boxed{ENTER}$. Next, move the cursor to the right of the same x-intercept, and press $\boxed{ENTER}$ twice. Repeat to find the other x-intercept.

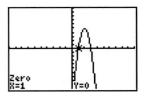 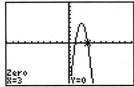

The t-intercepts are $t = 1$ and $t = 3$.

Step 5
Determine the solution to the inequality.

The solution to the inequality $-14.7 + 19.6t - 4.9t^2 < 0$ consists of the t-values, where $h < 0$ (below the x-axis), for the graph of $h = -14.7 + 19.6t - 4.9t^2$.

From the graph, it can be seen that the rock is less than 39.2 m above the river when $t < 1$ and $t > 3$. However, since time cannot be negative, the solution is 0 s $< t < 1$ s and $t > 3$ s.

7. If the amount of juice A, in millilitres, is represented by x and the amount of juice B, in millilitres, is represented by y, then the amount of juice that Lisa can drink each day can be represented by the inequality $0.15x + 0.40y \le 114$.

8. The inequality that must be represented is $0.15x + 0.40y \leq 114$. The solution consists of all ordered pairs on the line $0.15x + 0.40y = 114$, as well as ordered pairs that lie in the region bounded by $0.15x + 0.40y = 114$, the x-axis, and the y-axis. Solutions are limited to positive values since millilitres (mL) is a positive unit of measure.

The ordered pairs represent the amount of juice A (x-coordinates) and juice B(y-coordinates) that Lisa can drink.

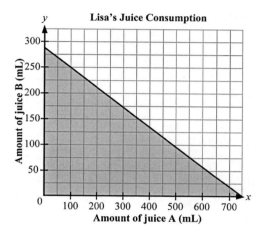

Lisa's Juice Consumption

ANSWERS AND SOLUTIONS

1. **Step 1**
Find the common difference, d.
$d = t_2 - t_1$
$d = -4 - 15$
$d = -19$

Step 2
Add the common difference five times to the last known term value.

Add -19 to -23 to get the next number in the sequence, and then add -19 four more times.
$-42, -61, -80, -99, -118$

2. **Step 1**
Identify the values of a and d for the given sequence.

The value of a is 3.5, and the value of d is -1.5.

Step 2
Write the general term formula for the given sequence.

Substitute $a = 3.5$ and $d = -1.5$ into the general term formula, and simplify.
$t_n = a + (n-1)d$
$t_n = 3.5 + (n-1)(-1.5)$
$t_n = 3.5 - 1.5n + 1.5$
$t_n = -1.5n + 5$

Step 3
Find the required term.
$t_n = -1.5n + 5$
$t_{30} = -1.5(30) + 5$
$t_{30} = -40$

3. **Step 1**
Find t_1 and t_2 using the given general term formula.

$t_n = 6n - 2$	$t_n = 6n - 2$
$t_1 = 6(1) - 2$	$t_2 = 6(2) - 2$
$t_1 = 4$	$t_2 = 10$

Step 2

Find the common difference, d.

$d = t_2 - t_1$
$d = 10 - 4$
$d = 6$

The first term is 4, and the common difference is 6.

4. **Step 1**

Find the common difference, d.

To insert five terms, use the general term formula to solve for d if $a = 17$ and $t_7 = -19$.

$17, \_\_, \_\_, \_\_, \_\_, \_\_, -19$

$t_n = a + (n-1)d$
$-19 = 17 + (7-1)d$
$-19 = 17 + 6d$
$-36 = 6d$
$-6 = d$

Step 2

Add the common difference to find the second, third, fourth, fifth, and sixth terms in the sequence.

Add -6 repeatedly.
$17, 11, 5, -1, -7, -13, -19$

5. **Step 1**

Use the first three terms of the sequence to determine the value of x.

Use the fact that the common difference is constant for all successive terms in an arithmetic sequence to write an equation.

$d = d$
$t_2 - t_1 = t_3 - t_2$
$7x - (x+6) = (9x+2) - 7x$
$7x - x - 6 = 9x + 2 - 7x$
$6x - 6 = 2x + 2$
$4x = 8$
$x = 2$

Step 2

Determine the numerical values of the first three terms of the sequence.

Substitute $x = 2$ into $(x + 6)$, $(7x)$, and $(9x + 2)$.

$x + 6$	$7x$	$9x + 2$
$= 2 + 6$	$= 7(2)$	$= 9(2) + 2$
$= 8$	$= 14$	$= 20$

The sequence is 8, 14, 20.

6. Substitute $d = 0.15$, $n = 5$, and $t_5 = 1.8$ into the general term formula, and solve for a.

$t_n = a + (n-1)d$
$1.8 = a + (5-1)(0.15)$
$1.8 = a + 0.75 - 0.15$
$1.2 = a$

Ice-cream cones cost $1.20 in the 1st year.

7. Find t_9 using the general term formula.
$t_n = a + (n-1)d$
$t_9 = 1.2 + (8)(0.15)$
$t_9 = 1.2 + 1.2$
$t_9 = 2.4$

In the 9th year, ice-cream cones will cost $2.40.

8. Find n if $t_n = 3.45$ using the general term formula.
$t_n = a + (n-1)d$
$3.45 = 1.2 + (n-1)(0.15)$
$3.45 = 1.2 + 0.15n - 0.15$
$2.4 = 0.15n$
$16 = n$

Ice-cream cones will cost $3.45 in the 16th year.

9. Find the common difference.
$d = t_2 - t_1$
$d = 1 - (-4)$
$d = 5$

Since the common difference of an arithmetic sequence and the slope of the graph of the related linear function are equal, the slope is 5.

Arithmetic Series

ANSWERS AND SOLUTIONS

1. Find the sum, where $a = 10$, $n = 8$, and $t_8 = -144$.

$$S_n = \frac{n}{2}(a + t_n)$$
$$S_8 = \frac{8}{2}(10 + (-144))$$
$$S_8 = 4(-134)$$
$$S_8 = -536$$

2. Find the sum, where $a = \frac{2}{5}$, $n = 11$, and $d = \frac{2}{5}$.

$$S_n = \frac{n}{2}\left[2a + (n-1)d\right]$$
$$S_{11} = \frac{11}{2}\left[2\left(\frac{2}{5}\right) + (11-1)\frac{2}{5}\right]$$
$$S_{11} = \frac{11}{2}\left(\frac{24}{5}\right)$$
$$S_{11} = \frac{132}{5}$$

3. Find the sum, where $a = 2$, $n = 6$, and $d = 3$.

$$S_n = \frac{n}{2}\left[2a + (n-1)d\right]$$
$$S_6 = \frac{6}{2}\left[2(2) + (6-1)3\right]$$
$$S_6 = 3(19)$$
$$S_6 = 57$$

Arnold will eat 57 treats in 6 days.

4. If Arnold eats 57 treats, then the remaining number of treats is $71 - 57 = 14$.

Arnold will give 14 treats to his siblings after the 6th day.

5. Find the 9th term of the series, where $S_8 = 14$ and $S_9 = 27$.

$$t_n = S_n - S_{n-1}$$
$$t_9 = S_9 - S_8$$
$$t_9 = 27 - 14$$
$$t_9 = 13$$

The 9th term of the series is 13.

6. Step 1

Before either sum formula can be used, find the number of terms in the series using the general term formula, where $a = 15$, $d = 3$, and $t_n = 45$.

$$t_n = a + (n-1)d$$
$$45 = 15 + (n-1)(3)$$
$$45 = 15 + 3n - 3$$
$$33 = 3n$$
$$11 = n$$

Step 2

Use the sum formula $S_n = \frac{n}{2}(a + t_n)$ to find the sum of the 11 terms.

$$S_n = \frac{n}{2}(a + t_n)$$
$$S_{11} = \frac{11}{2}(15 + 45)$$
$$S_{11} = \frac{11}{2}(60)$$
$$S_{11} = 330$$

7. Since the sum of the series is known, use the sum formula $S_n = \frac{n}{2}\left[2a + (n-1)d\right]$ to find the common difference, where $S_{10} = -55$ and $a = t_1 = 8$.

$$S_n = \frac{n}{2}\left[2a + (n-1)d\right]$$
$$-55 = \frac{10}{2}\left[2(8) + (10-1)d\right]$$
$$-55 = 5\left[16 + 9d\right]$$
$$-55 = 80 + 45d$$
$$-135 = 45d$$
$$-3 = d$$

Geometric Sequences

PRACTICE EXERCISES
ANSWERS AND SOLUTIONS

1. **Step 1**
   Find the common ratio.

   $$r = \frac{t_2}{t_1}$$

   $$r = \frac{3}{\sqrt{3}}$$

   $$r = \frac{3}{\sqrt{3}} \times \frac{\sqrt{3}}{\sqrt{3}}$$

   $$r = \frac{3\sqrt{3}}{3}$$

   $$r = \sqrt{3}$$

   If the common ratio is found using t_3 and t_2, rationalizing the denominator is not necessary.

   $$r = \frac{t_3}{t_2}$$

   $$r = \frac{3\sqrt{3}}{3}$$

   $$r = \sqrt{3}$$

   Step 2
   Repeatedly multiply the common ratio by the previous term to find the next three terms.

   $$t_4 = \sqrt{3}\left(3\sqrt{3}\right)$$
   $$t_4 = 9$$

   $$t_5 = \sqrt{3}(9)$$
   $$t_5 = 9\sqrt{3}$$

   $$t_6 = \sqrt{3}\left(9\sqrt{3}\right)$$
   $$t_6 = 27$$

   The geometric sequence is $\sqrt{3}$, 3, $3\sqrt{3}$, 9, $9\sqrt{3}$, 27,....

2. **Step 1**
   Find the common ratio.

   If David keeps 100% of his current wage and earns a 6%/h increase each year, he will earn 106%/h of what he made the previous year.

   Therefore, the common ratio will be 1.06.

Step 2
Find subsequent hourly wages by repeatedly multiplying the common ratio by the hourly wage.
Year 1: wage = $9.85
Year 2: wage = $9.85 × 1.06 = $10.44
Year 3: wage = $10.44 × 1.06 = $11.07

He will earn $11.07/h in year 3.

3. Continue the pattern until the wage exceeds $13.00/h.
   Year 4: wage = $11.07 × 1.06 = $11.73
   Year 5: wage = $11.73 × 1.06 = $12.44
   Year 6: wage = $12.44 × 1.06 = $13.18

   In his sixth year, David will earn more than $13.00/h.

4. **Step 1**
   Find the common ratio.

   If the motorcycle depreciates 16%, it is maintaining 84% of its value. The common ratio is 0.84.

   Step 2
   Find subsequent motorcycle values by repeatedly multiplying the common ratio by the previous motorcycle value.

   Find the year when the value of the motorcycle first drops below $4 000.
   Year 1: value = $8 000
   Year 2: value = $8 000 × 0.84 = $6 720
   Year 3: value = $6 720 × 0.84 = $5 644.80
   Year 4: value = $5 644.80 × 0.84 = $4 741.63
   Year 5: value = $4 741.63 × 0.84 = $3 982.97

   Amorita will own the motorcycle until the fifth year when it becomes worth less than half of its original value and she decides to sell it.

5. Find t_1 by substituting $n = 1$ into the general term formula $t_n = 2(3)^{n-1}$. Repeat for t_2, t_3, and t_4.

   $$t_1 = 2(3)^{1-1} = 2$$
   $$t_2 = 2(3)^{2-1} = 6$$
   $$t_3 = 2(3)^{3-1} = 18$$
   $$t_4 = 2(3)^{4-1} = 54$$

   The first four terms of the sequence are 2, 6, 18, and 54.

6. Step 1

Use the first three terms of the sequence to determine the value of x.

Use the fact that the common ratio is constant between terms to write an equation that can be solved for x.

$$r = r$$
$$\frac{t_2}{t_1} = \frac{t_3}{t_2}$$
$$\frac{x+2}{x} = \frac{x+5}{x+2}$$
$$(x+2)(x+2) = (x)(x+5)$$
$$x^2 + 4x + 4 = x^2 + 5x$$
$$4 = x$$

Step 2

Find the values of the terms of the sequence.

Substitute $x = 4$ into the first three terms given by x, $x + 2$, and $x + 5$.

$x = 4$	$x + 2$	$x + 5$
	$= 4 + 2$	$= 4 + 5$
	$= 6$	$= 9$

The first three terms of the sequence are 4, 6, and 9.

Step 3

Find the common ratio of the sequence.

$$r = \frac{t_2}{t_1}$$
$$r = \frac{6}{4}$$
$$r = \frac{3}{2}$$

7. Substitute $n = 1$ into the general term to find t_1.

$$t_n = -6\,161(-0.235)^{n-1}$$
$$t_1 = -6\,161(-0.235)^{1-1}$$
$$t_1 = -6\,161$$

8. Step 1

Identify the values of a and r for the given sequence.

The value of a (the first term) is $-\frac{1}{8}$.

$$r = \frac{t_2}{t_1}$$
$$r = \frac{1}{10} \div -\frac{1}{8}$$
$$r = \frac{1}{10} \times -\frac{8}{1}$$
$$r = -\frac{4}{5}$$

Step 2

Write the general term formula for the given sequence.

Substitute $a = -\frac{1}{8}$ and $r = -\frac{4}{5}$ into the general term formula.

$$t_n = ar^{n-1}$$
$$t_n = -\frac{1}{8}\left(-\frac{4}{5}\right)^{n-1}$$

9. Step 1

Express each term using the general term formula $t_n = ar^{n-1}$.

$t_3 = ar^{3-1}$	and	$t_6 = ar^{6-1}$
$t_3 = ar^2$		$t_6 = ar^5$
$10\,000 = ar^2$		$5\,120 = ar^5$

Step 2

Express $5\,120 = ar^5$ and $10\,000 = ar^2$ as two equivalent ratios.

$$\frac{ar^5}{ar^2} = \frac{5\,120}{10\,000}$$

Step 3

Solve for r.

$$\frac{ar^5}{ar^2} = \frac{5\,120}{10\,000}$$
$$r^3 = \frac{64}{125}$$
$$r = \sqrt[3]{\frac{64}{125}}$$
$$r = \frac{4}{5}$$

Step 4
Write the general term formula for the given sequence.

Find a by substituting $r = \dfrac{4}{5}$ into the equation $10\ 000 = ar^2$.

$$10\ 000 = a\left(\dfrac{4}{5}\right)^2$$
$$10\ 000 = \dfrac{16}{25}a$$
$$15\ 625 = a$$

Substituting the values of a and r into the formula $t_n = ar^{n-1}$, the general term is $t_n = 15\ 625\left(\dfrac{4}{5}\right)^{n-1}$.

Step 5
Find the required term.

Use the general term for this sequence.

$$t_n = 15\ 625\left(\dfrac{4}{5}\right)^{n-1}$$
$$t_8 = 15\ 625\left(\dfrac{4}{5}\right)^{7}$$
$$t_8 = \dfrac{16\ 384}{5} \text{ or } 3\ 276.8$$

Geometric Series

ANSWERS AND SOLUTIONS

1. **Step 1**
    Identify the known quantities, and choose a sum formula.

    The known quantities are $a = 7$, $t_n = -3\ 584$, and $r = \dfrac{-14}{7} = -2$. Therefore, the formula

    $S_n = \dfrac{rt_n - a}{r - 1}$ should be used to find S_n.

Step 2
Substitute the known quantities into $S_n = \dfrac{rt_n - a}{r - 1}$, and solve for S_n.

$$S_n = \dfrac{rt_n - a}{r - 1}$$
$$S_n = \dfrac{(-2)(-3\ 584) - 7}{-2 - 1}$$
$$S_n = \dfrac{7\ 161}{-3}$$
$$S_n = -2\ 387$$

The sum of the geometric series is $-2\ 387$.

2. **Step 1**
    Use the general term to find a, r, and t_8.

    Since the general term $t_n = -4(-3)^{n-1}$ is in the form $t_n = ar^{n-1}$, $a = -4$ and $r = -3$.

    Find t_8 by substituting $n = 8$ into the general term.
    $$t_n = -4(-3)^{n-1}$$
    $$t_8 = -4(-3)^{8-1}$$
    $$t_8 = -4(-3)^{7}$$
    $$t_8 = 8\ 748$$

Step 2
Substitute the known quantities into $S_n = \dfrac{rt_n - a}{r - 1}$, and solve for S_n.

$$S_8 = \dfrac{(-3)(8\ 748) - (-4)}{(-3) - 1}$$
$$S_8 = 6\ 560$$

The sum of the first eight terms is $6\ 560$.

3. **Step 1**
    Identify the known quantities, and choose a sum formula.
    The known quantities are $a = -2$, $S_n = -7\ 812$, and $r = 5$. Therefore, the formula $S_n = \dfrac{a(r^n - 1)}{r - 1}$ should be used to find n.

    Step 2
    Substitute the known quantities into $S_n = \dfrac{a(r^n - 1)}{r - 1}$, and solve for n by guessing and checking.

$$-7\,812 = \frac{-2\left(5^n - 1\right)}{5 - 1}$$

$$-7\,812 = \frac{-2\left(5^n - 1\right)}{4}$$

$$-7\,812 = \frac{5^n - 1}{-2}$$

$$15\,624 = 5^n - 1$$

$$15\,625 = 5^n$$

$$15\,625 = 5^6$$

$$15\,625 = 15\,625$$

The value of n is 6, so there are six terms in the series.

4. **Step 1**

   Identify the known quantities, and choose a sum formula.

   The known quantities are $S_4 = 2\,862$ and $r = 3.5$.

   Therefore, the formula $S_n = \dfrac{a(r^n - 1)}{r - 1}$ should be used to find a.

   Step 2

   Substitute the known quantities into

   $S_n = \dfrac{a(r^n - 1)}{r - 1}$, and solve for a.

   $$2\,862 = \frac{a\left((3.5)^4 - 1\right)}{3.5 - 1}$$

   $$2\,862 = \frac{a\left(149.0625\right)}{2.5}$$

   $$7\,155 = a\left(149.0625\right)$$

   $$48 = a$$

   The first term in the series is 48.

5. **Step 1**

   Find the value of the common ratio, r.

   Since $t_4 = 54$ and $t_6 = 24$, then $ar^3 = 54$ and $ar^5 = 24$. Express $ar^5 = 24$ and $ar^3 = 54$ as two equivalent ratios.

   $$\frac{ar^5}{ar^3} = \frac{24}{54}$$

   $$r^2 = \frac{4}{9}$$

   $$r = \pm\frac{2}{3}$$

Step 2

Find the value of the first term, a.

If $r = +\dfrac{2}{3}$:

$$ar^3 = 54$$

$$a\left(\frac{2}{3}\right)^3 = 54$$

$$a\left(\frac{8}{27}\right) = 54$$

$$a = 182.25$$

If $r = -\dfrac{2}{3}$:

$$ar^3 = 54$$

$$a\left(-\frac{2}{3}\right)^3 = 54$$

$$a\left(-\frac{8}{27}\right) = 54$$

$$a = -182.25$$

Therefore, $a = 182.25$ when $r = \dfrac{2}{3}$, and

$a = -182.25$ when $r = -\dfrac{2}{3}$.

Step 3

Substitute the known quantities into

$S_n = \dfrac{a\left(r^n - 1\right)}{r - 1}$, and find $S14$ for both

possible cases.

When $a = 182.25$ and $r = \dfrac{2}{3}$:

$$S_{14} = \frac{182.25\left(\left(\frac{2}{3}\right)^{14} - 1\right)}{\frac{2}{3} - 1}$$

$$S_{14} \doteq \frac{-181.6257}{-0.3333}$$

$$S_{14} \doteq 544.9$$

When $a = -182.25$ and $r = -\dfrac{2}{3}$:

$$S_{14} = \frac{-182.25\left(\left(-\frac{2}{3}\right)^{14} - 1\right)}{-\frac{2}{3} - 1}$$

$$S_{14} \doteq \frac{181.6257}{-1.6667}$$

$$S_{14} \doteq -109.0$$

Therefore, the sum of the first 14 terms in the series will either be 544.9 or −109.0.

6. **Step 1**
Find the values of t_1 and t_2.

If $S_1 = 18$, $t_1 = 18$.

Using the formula $t_n = S_n - S_{n-1}$, the value of t_2 can be found.
$$t_2 = S_2 - S_1$$
$$t_2 = 6 - 18$$
$$t_2 = -12$$

Step 2
Find the common ratio.
$$r = \frac{t_2}{t_1}$$
$$r = \frac{-12}{18}$$
$$r = \frac{-2}{3}$$

Step 3
Write the general term using the known values of a and r.

The general term is $t_n = 18\left(-\frac{2}{3}\right)^{n-1}$.

7. **Step 1**
Determine if the infinite series is convergent.

Find the common ratio.
$$r = \frac{t_2}{t_1}$$
$$r = \frac{2\,500}{3\,125}$$
$$r = 0.8$$

The series is convergent since $-1 < r < 1$.

Step 2
Find the sum of the series using the formula for the sum of an infinite geometric series $S_\infty = \frac{a}{1-r}$.

Substitute $a = 3\,125$ and $r = 0.8$.

$$S_\infty = \frac{a}{1-r}$$
$$S_\infty = \frac{3\,125}{1-0.8}$$
$$S_\infty = \frac{3\,125}{0.2}$$
$$S_\infty = 15\,625$$

The sum of the infinite geometric series is 15 625.

8. **Step 1**
Use the sum formula $S_n = n - 5n^2$ to find S_1, S_2, and S_3.
$$S_1 = 1 - 5(1)^2 = -4$$
$$S_2 = 2 - 5(2)^2 = -18$$
$$S_3 = 3 - 5(3)^2 = -42$$

Step 2
Find the value of t_1, t_2, and t_3 using the formula $t_n = S_n - S_{n-1}$.
$$t_1 = S_1 = -4$$

$$t_2 = S_2 - S_1$$
$$t_2 = -18 - (-4)$$
$$t_2 = -14$$

$$t_3 = S_3 - S_2$$
$$t_3 = -42 - (-18)$$
$$t_3 = -24$$

The series is −4 −14 −24 ...

Step 3
Determine if the series is geometric.

A series is geometric if there is a common ratio.
$$\frac{t_2}{t_1} = \frac{-14}{-4} = \frac{7}{2}$$
$$\frac{t_3}{t_2} = \frac{-24}{-14} = \frac{12}{7}$$

Therefore, the series is not geometric because $\frac{t_2}{t_1} \neq \frac{t_3}{t_2}$.

Topic Practice Questions

ANSWERS AND SOLUTIONS

1. Since the sequence is decreasing by 2, then 3, and then 4, it is neither geometric nor arithmetic.

2. Since the common ratio is 4, it is a geometric sequence.

3. Since the common difference is –1.5, it is an arithmetic sequence.

4. Since successive terms are written with an additional digit of 1, it is neither geometric nor arithmetic.

5. Since the common ratio is $\sqrt{7}$, it is a geometric sequence.

6. Since the common difference is $\frac{2}{3}$, it is an arithmetic sequence.

7. **Step 1**
   Find the general term, t_n, by substituting the values for a and d into the general term formula.
   $a = 3.5$

   $d = -1.5 - 3.5$
   $d = -5$

   $t_n = a + (n-1)d$
   $t_n = 3.5 + (n-1)(-5)$
   $t_n = -5n + 8.5$

   Step 2
   Substitute $n = 10$ into the general term formula to find t_{10}.
   $t_n = -5n + 8.5$
   $t_{10} = -5(10) + 8.5$
   $t_{10} = -41.5$

Step 3
Substitute $a = 3.5$ and $t_{10} = -41.5$ into

$S_n = \frac{n}{2}(a + t_n)$ to find S_{10}.

$S_n = \frac{n}{2}(a + t_n)$
$S_{10} = \frac{10}{2}(3.5 + (-41.5))$
$S_{10} = 5(-38)$
$S_{10} = -190$

8. Since $S_{15} = 48$ and $S_{14} = 32$, t_{15} can be found using the formula $t_n = S_n - S_{(n-1)}$.
   $t_{15} = S_{15} - S_{14}$
   $t_{15} = 48 - 32$
   $t_{15} = 16$

9. If $d = 6$, $n = 10$, and $t_{10} = 61$, use the general term formula to find a.
   $t_n = a + (n-1)d$
   $61 = a + (10-1)(6)$
   $61 = a + 54$
   $7 = a$

   There were 7 members in the first week.

10. If $a = 9$ and $d = 6$, use the general term formula to find t_7.
    $t_n = a + (n-1)d$
    $t_7 = 9 + (7-1)(6)$
    $t_7 = 45$

    Theresa pulls 45 weeds on the 7th day.

11. If $a = 9$ and $t_7 = 45$, use the sum formula

    $S_n = \frac{n}{2}(a + t_n)$ to find S_7.

    $S_n = \frac{n}{2}(a + t_n)$
    $S_7 = \frac{7}{2}(9 + 45)$
    $S_7 = 189$

    Theresa has pulled 189 weeds in total by the end of the 7th day.

12. **Step 1**
    Find d using the general term formula.
    Temporarily consider $t_4 = 46$ and $t_{12} = 102$ as the

first and last terms of a sequence. This means the terms can be rewritten as $t_1 = 46$ and $t_9 = 102$ and the general term formula can be used.

$$t_n = a + (n-1)d$$
$$102 = 46 + (9-1)(d)$$
$$102 = 46 + 8d$$
$$56 = 8d$$
$$7 = d$$

Step 2
Find the actual value of a for the sequence where $t_4 = 46$ and $d = 7$.

$$t_n = a + (n-1)d$$
$$46 = a + (4-1)(7)$$
$$46 = a + 21$$
$$25 = a$$

Step 3
Solve for n if $t_n < 150$ using the general term formula.

$$a + (n-1)d = t_n$$
$$25 + (n-1)(7) < 150$$
$$25 + 7n - 7 < 150$$
$$7n < 132$$
$$n < 18.8571...$$

There are 18 terms less than 150 in the sequence.

13. **Step 1**
Find the common ratio, r.

If the car loses 17% of its value each year, it maintains 83%, which means $r = 0.83$.

Step 2
Find subsequent car values by repeatedly multiplying the common ratio by the previous car value.

Multiply by the common ratio to obtain the value of the car at the end of each year.
Year 1: $32\ 000 \times 0.83 = \$26\ 560$
Year 2: $26\ 560 \times 0.83 = \$22\ 044.80$
Year 3: $22\ 044.8 \times 0.83 = \$18\ 297.18$

Therefore, the car's value at the end of three years is \$18 297.18.

14. **Step 1**
Identify the values of a and r.

The known values are $a = -3$ and $r = \dfrac{t_2}{t_1} = \dfrac{2}{-3}$.

Step 2
Find the general term.

$$t_n = a(r)^{n-1}$$
$$t_n = -3\left(-\frac{2}{3}\right)^{n-1}$$

15. **Step 1**
Identify the values of a and r from the general term.

Since $t_n = -3(-2)^{n-1}$ is in the form $t_n = ar^{n-1}$, $a = -3$ and $r = -2$.

Step 2
Substitute the values for a and r into the sum formula $S_n = \dfrac{a(r^n - 1)}{r - 1}$ to find S_{10}.

$$S_n = \frac{a(r^n - 1)}{r - 1}$$
$$S_{10} = \frac{-3((-2)^{10} - 1)}{-2 - 1}$$
$$S_{10} = 1\ 023$$

16. **Step 1**
Find a and r using the sums of $S_1 = 36$ and $S_2 = 24$ and the formula $t_n = S_n - S_{(n-1)}$.

$$t_1 = S_1 = 36$$
$$t_2 = S_2 - S_1$$
$$t_2 = 24 - 36$$
$$t_2 = -12$$

$$r = \frac{t_2}{t_1}$$
$$r = \frac{-12}{36}$$
$$r = -\frac{1}{3}$$

Step 2
Write the general term of the series.

$$a = 36 \text{ and } r = -\frac{1}{3}$$
$$t_n = ar^{n-1}$$
$$t_n = 36\left(-\frac{1}{3}\right)^{n-1}$$

17. Step 1
Find the value of the common ratio, r.
If $t_3 + t_4 = 50$, then $ar^2 + ar^3 = 50$.
If $t_4 + t_5 = 100$, then $ar^3 + ar^4 = 100$.

Express $ar^3 + ar^4 = 100$ and $ar^2 + ar^3 = 50$ as two equivalent ratios.

$$\frac{ar^3 + ar^4}{ar^2 + ar^3} = \frac{100}{50}$$
$$\frac{ar^3(1+r)}{ar^2(1+r)} = 2$$
$$r = 2$$

Step 2
Find the value of the first term, a.

Substitute $r = 2$ and $ar^2 + ar^3 = 50$.

$$a(2)^2 + a(2)^3 = 50$$
$$4a + 8a = 50$$
$$12a = 50$$
$$a = \frac{50}{12}$$
$$a = \frac{25}{6}$$

Therefore, $t_1 = \frac{25}{6}$ and $t_2 = \frac{25}{6} \times 2$, which is

$t_2 = \frac{25}{3}$.

18. Step 1
Find the total distance that the ball falls.

The series is $12 + 8 + \frac{16}{3} + \ldots$,

where $t_1 = 12$, $t_2 = 8$, and $t_3 = \frac{16}{3}$.

Therefore, $a = 12$ and $r = \frac{2}{3}$.

Since the ball falls 8 times, $n = 8$.

Use the sum formula $S_n = \frac{a(r^n - 1)}{r - 1}$ to find S_8.

$$S_n = \frac{a(r^n - 1)}{r - 1}$$
$$S_8 = \frac{12\left(\left(\frac{2}{3}\right)^8 - 1\right)}{\left(\frac{2}{3}\right) - 1}$$
$$S_8 \doteq 34.60$$

Step 2
Find the total distance that the ball rises.

If the ball rises to a height of 8 m after the first bounce, then $t_1 = 8$, $t_2 = \frac{16}{3}$, and $t_3 = \frac{32}{9}$.

Therefore, $a = 8$ and $r = \frac{2}{3}$.

Since the ball rises 7 times, $n = 7$.

Use the sum formula $S_n = \frac{a(r^n - 1)}{r - 1}$ to find S_7.

$$S_n = \frac{a(r^n - 1)}{r - 1}$$
$$S_7 = \frac{8\left(\left(\frac{2}{3}\right)^7 - 1\right)}{\left(\frac{2}{3}\right) - 1}$$
$$S_7 \doteq 22.60$$

Step 3
Find the total vertical distance travelled by the ball.

total distance = total distance rising + total distance falling
total distance $\doteq 22.60 + 34.60 \doteq 57.20$

Therefore, the ball has travelled approximately 57.2 m when it hits the ground for the 8th time.

RECIPROCAL FUNCTIONS

Asymptotes

ANSWERS AND SOLUTIONS

1. The horizontal asymptote of the function is at $y = 0$.

    Determine the vertical asymptotes.

    Set the denominator equal to zero, and solve for x.
    $$9x + 6 = 0$$
    $$9x = -6$$
    $$x = \frac{-6}{9}$$
    $$x = -\frac{2}{3}$$

    The vertical asymptote is at $x = -\frac{2}{3}$.

2. The horizontal asymptote of the function is at $y = 0$.

    Determine the vertical asymptotes.

    Set the denominator equal to zero, and solve for x.
    $$10x - 13 = 0$$
    $$10x = 13$$
    $$x = \frac{13}{10}$$
    $$x = 1.3$$

    The vertical asymptote is at $x = \frac{13}{10}$ or $x = 1.3$.

3. Rewrite the function $y = -\dfrac{1}{6x + 54}$

    as $y = \dfrac{1}{-(6x + 54)}$.

    The horizontal asymptote of the function is at $y = 0$.

    Determine the vertical asymptotes.

    Set the denominator equal to zero, and solve for x.

$$-(6x + 54) = 0$$
$$6x + 54 = 0$$
$$6x = -54$$
$$x = -9$$

The vertical asymptote is at $x = -9$.

4. The horizontal asymptote of the function is at $y = 0$.

    Determine the vertical asymptotes.

    Set the denominator equal to zero, and solve for x.
    $$x^2 + 3x - 4 = 0$$
    $$x^2 - x + 4x - 4 = 0$$
    $$x(x - 1) + 4(x - 1) = 0$$
    $$(x - 1)(x + 4) = 0$$
    $$x - 1 = 0 \qquad x + 4 = 0$$
    $$x = 1 \qquad x = -4$$

    The vertical asymptotes are at $x = 1$ and $x = -4$.

5. The horizontal asymptote of the function is at $y = 0$.

    Determine the vertical asymptotes.

    Set the denominator equal to zero, and solve for x.
    $$121x^2 - 144 = 0$$
    $$121x^2 = 144$$
    $$x^2 = \frac{144}{121}$$
    $$x = \pm\sqrt{\frac{144}{121}}$$
    $$x = \pm\frac{12}{11}$$

    The vertical asymptotes are at $x = \frac{12}{11}$

    and $x = -\frac{12}{11}$.

6. The horizontal asymptote of the function is at $y = 0$.

    Determine the vertical asymptotes.

Set the denominator equal to zero, and solve for x.
$$10x^2 - 14x + 4 = 0$$
$$2(5x^2 - 7x + 2) = 0$$
$$5x^2 - 7x + 2 = 0,$$
$$5x^2 - 5x - 2x + 2 = 0$$
$$5x(x-1) - 2(x-1) = 0$$
$$(x-1)(5x-2) = 0$$

$$\begin{array}{ll} x - 1 = 0 & 5x - 2 = 0 \\ x = 1 & 5x = 2 \\ & x = \dfrac{2}{5} \\ & x = 0.4 \end{array}$$

The vertical asymptotes are at $x = 1$ and $x = \dfrac{2}{5}$ or $x = 0.4$.

The Behaviour of the Graph of a Reciprocal Function

ANSWERS AND SOLUTIONS

1. Invariant points will occur when the y-coordinate of any ordered pair on the graph of $f(x) = x + 5$ is equal to 1 or -1.

If $y = 1$:   If $y = -1$:
$$1 = x + 5 \qquad\qquad -1 = x + 5$$
$$-4 = x \qquad\qquad\quad -6 = x$$

Therefore, $(-4, 1)$ and $(-6, -1)$ are invariant points.

Step 1
Determine the vertical asymptote. Set the denominator equal to zero, and solve for x.
$$x + 5 = 0$$
$$x = -5$$

There is a vertical asymptote at $x = -5$.

Step 2
Determine the behaviour of the graph on the left of $x = -5$. Calculate values of y as x approaches -5 from the left.

If $x = -5.01$:   If $x = -5.0001$:

$$y = \frac{1}{x+5} \qquad\qquad y = \frac{1}{x+5}$$
$$y = \frac{1}{-5.01+5} \qquad y = \frac{1}{-5.0001+5}$$
$$y = \frac{1}{-0.01} \qquad\quad y = \frac{1}{-0.0001}$$
$$y = -100 \qquad\qquad y = -10\,000$$

The y-values get smaller and smaller toward negative infinity.

Step 3
Determine the behaviour of the graph on the right of $x = -5$.

Calculate values of y as x approaches -5 from the right.
If $x = -4.99$:   If $x = -4.9999$:

$$y = \frac{1}{x+5} \qquad\qquad y = \frac{1}{x+5}$$
$$y = \frac{1}{(-4.99)+5} \qquad y = \frac{1}{(-4.9999)+5}$$
$$y = \frac{1}{0.01} \qquad\qquad y = \frac{1}{0.0001}$$
$$y = 100 \qquad\qquad y = 10\,000$$

The y-values get larger and larger toward positive infinity.

Step 4
Determine the behaviour of the graph as $x \to -\infty$.
If $x = -10$:   If $x = -200$:

$$y = \frac{1}{x+5} \qquad\qquad y = \frac{1}{x+5}$$
$$y = \frac{1}{-10+5} \qquad y = \frac{1}{-200+5}$$
$$y = \frac{1}{-5} \qquad\qquad y = \frac{1}{-195}$$

The y-values approach zero, but remain negative. The x-axis becomes a horizontal asymptote as $x \to -\infty$.

Step 5
Determine the behaviour of the graph as $x \to \infty$.
If $x = 10$:   If $x = 200$:

$$y = \frac{1}{x+5} \qquad\qquad y = \frac{1}{x+5}$$
$$y = \frac{1}{10+5} \qquad y = \frac{1}{200+5}$$
$$y = \frac{1}{15} \qquad\qquad y = \frac{1}{205}$$

The y-values approach zero, but remain positive. The x-axis becomes the horizontal asymptote as $x \to \infty$.

2. Invariant points will occur when the y-coordinate of any ordered pair on the graph of $f(x) = 4x - 28$ is equal to 1 or -1.

If $y = 1$:
$$1 = 4x - 28$$
$$29 = 4x$$
$$\frac{29}{4} = x$$
$$7.25 = x$$

If $y = -1$:
$$-1 = 4x - 28$$
$$27 = 4x$$
$$\frac{27}{4} = x$$
$$6.75 = x$$

Therefore, $(7.25, 1)$ and $(6.75, -1)$ are invariant points.

Step 1
Determine the vertical asymptote.

Set the denominator equal to zero, and solve for x.
$$4x - 28 = 0$$
$$4x = 28$$
$$x = 7$$

There is a vertical asymptote at $x = 7$.

Step 2
Determine the behaviour of the graph on the left of $x = 7$.

Calculate values of y as x approaches 7 from the left.

If $x = 6.99$:
$$y = \frac{1}{4x - 28}$$
$$y = \frac{1}{4(6.99) - 28}$$
$$y = \frac{1}{-0.04}$$
$$y = -25$$

If $x = 6.9999$:
$$y = \frac{1}{4x - 28}$$
$$y = \frac{1}{4(6.9999) - 28}$$
$$y = \frac{1}{-0.0004}$$
$$y = -2\ 500$$

The y-values get smaller and smaller toward negative infinity.

Step 3
Determine the behaviour of the graph on the right of $x = 7$.

Calculate values of y as x approaches 7 from the right.

If $x = 7.01$:
$$y = \frac{1}{4x - 28}$$
$$y = \frac{1}{4(7.01) - 28}$$
$$y = \frac{1}{0.04}$$
$$y = 25$$

If $x = 7.0001$:
$$y = \frac{1}{4x - 28}$$
$$y = \frac{1}{4(7.0001) - 28}$$
$$y = \frac{1}{0.0004}$$
$$y = 2\ 500$$

The y-values get larger and larger toward positive infinity.

Step 4
Determine the behaviour of the graph as $x \to -\infty$.

If $x = -10$:
$$y = \frac{1}{4x - 28}$$
$$y = \frac{1}{4(-10) - 28}$$
$$y = \frac{1}{-68}$$

If $x = -200$:
$$y = \frac{1}{4x - 28}$$
$$y = \frac{1}{4(-200) - 28}$$
$$y = \frac{1}{-828}$$

The y-values approach zero, but remain negative. The x-axis becomes a horizontal asymptote as $x \to -\infty$.

Step 5
Determine the behaviour of the graph as $x \to \infty$.

If $x = 10$:
$$y = \frac{1}{4x - 28}$$
$$y = \frac{1}{4(10) - 28}$$
$$y = \frac{1}{12}$$

If $x = 200$:
$$y = \frac{1}{4x - 28}$$
$$y = \frac{1}{4(200) - 28}$$
$$y = \frac{1}{772}$$

The y-values approach zero, but remain positive. The x-axis becomes the horizontal asymptote as $x \to \infty$.

3. Invariant points will occur when the y-coordinate of any ordered pair on the graph of $f(x) = 2x^2 - 8$ is equal to 1 or -1.

If $y = 1$:
$$1 = 2x^2 - 8$$
$$9 = 2x^2$$
$$4.5 = x^2$$
$$\pm\sqrt{4.5} = x$$

If $y = -1$:
$$-1 = 2x^2 - 8$$
$$7 = 2x^2$$
$$3.5 = x^2$$
$$\pm\sqrt{3.5} = x$$

Therefore, $\left(-\sqrt{4.5}, 1\right)$, $\left(\sqrt{4.5}, 1\right)$, $\left(-\sqrt{3.5}, -1\right)$, and $\left(\sqrt{3.5}, -1\right)$ are invariant points.

Step 1
Determine the vertical asymptotes.

Set the denominator equal to zero, and solve for x.
$$0 = 2x^2 - 8$$
$$8 = 2x^2$$
$$4 = x^2$$
$$\pm\sqrt{4} = x$$
$$\pm 2 = x$$

The vertical asymptotes are at $x = -2$ and $x = 2$.

Step 2
Determine the behaviour of the graph on the left of $x = -2$.

Calculate values of y as x approaches -2 from the left.

If $x = -2.01$:
$$y = \frac{1}{2x^2 - 8}$$
$$y = \frac{1}{2(-2.01)^2 - 8}$$
$$y = \frac{1}{0.0802}$$
$$y \doteq 12.468\ 827\ 93$$

If $x = -2.001$:
$$y = \frac{1}{2x^2 - 8}$$
$$y = \frac{1}{2(-2.001)^2 - 8}$$
$$y = \frac{1}{0.008\ 002}$$
$$y \doteq 124.968\ 757\ 8$$

The y-values get larger and larger toward positive infinity.

Step 3
Determine the behaviour of the graph on the right of $x = -2$.

Calculate values of y as x approaches -2 from the right.

If $x = -1.99$:
$$y = \frac{1}{2x^2 - 8}$$
$$y = \frac{1}{2(-1.99)^2 - 8}$$
$$y = \frac{1}{-0.0798}$$
$$y \doteq -12.531\ 328\ 32$$

If $x = -1.9999$:
$$y = \frac{1}{2x^2 - 8}$$
$$y = \frac{1}{2(-1.999)^2 - 8}$$
$$y = \frac{1}{-0.007\ 998}$$
$$y \doteq -125.031\ 257\ 8$$

The y-values get smaller and smaller toward negative infinity.

Step 4
Determine the behaviour of the graph on the left of $x = 2$.

Calculate values of y as x approaches 2 from the left.

If $x = 1.99$:
$$y = \frac{1}{2x^2 - 8}$$
$$y = \frac{1}{2(1.99)^2 - 8}$$
$$y = \frac{1}{-0.0798}$$
$$y \doteq -12.531\ 328\ 32$$

If $x = 1.999$:
$$y = \frac{1}{2x^2 - 8}$$
$$y = \frac{1}{2(1.999)^2 - 8}$$
$$y = \frac{1}{-0.007\ 998}$$
$$y \doteq -125.031\ 257\ 8$$

The y-values get smaller and smaller toward negative infinity.

Step 5
Determine the behaviour of the graph on the right of $x = 2$.

Calculate values of y as x approaches 2 from the right.

If $x = 2.01$:
$$y = \frac{1}{2x^2 - 8}$$
$$y = \frac{1}{2(2.01)^2 - 8}$$
$$y = \frac{1}{0.0802}$$
$$y \doteq 12.468\ 827\ 93$$

If $x = 2.001$:
$$y = \frac{1}{2x^2 - 8}$$
$$y = \frac{1}{2(2.001)^2 - 8}$$
$$y = \frac{1}{0.008\ 002}$$
$$y \doteq 124.968\ 757\ 8$$

The y-values get larger and larger toward positive infinity.

Step 6
Determine the behaviour of the graph as $x \to -\infty$.

If $x = -10$:
$$y = \frac{1}{2x^2 - 8}$$
$$y = \frac{1}{2(-10)^2 - 8}$$
$$y = \frac{1}{192}$$

If $x = -200$:
$$y = \frac{1}{2x^2 - 8}$$
$$y = \frac{1}{2(-200)^2 - 8}$$
$$y = \frac{1}{79\ 992}$$

The y-values approach zero, but remain positive. The x-axis becomes a horizontal asymptote as $x \to -\infty$.

Step 7
Determine the behaviour of the graph as $x \to \infty$.

If $x = 10$:

$$y = \frac{1}{2x^2 - 8}$$
$$y = \frac{1}{2(10)^2 - 8}$$
$$y = \frac{1}{192}$$

If $x = 200$:

$$y = \frac{1}{2x^2 - 8}$$
$$y = \frac{1}{2(200)^2 - 8}$$
$$y = \frac{1}{79\ 992}$$

The y-values approach zero, but remain positive. The x-axis becomes a horizontal asymptote as $x \to \infty$.

Graphing Reciprocal Functions

ANSWERS AND SOLUTIONS

1. **Step 1**
Determine the vertical asymptote of the function $y = \frac{1}{2x + 2}$.

Solve for x when $2x + 2 = 0$.
$$2x + 2 = 0$$
$$2x = -2$$
$$x = -1$$

Therefore, the vertical asymptote occurs at $x = -1$. Sketch the vertical asymptote as a dotted line.

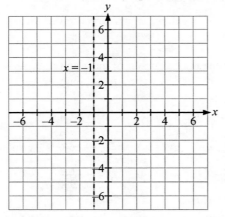

Step 2
Find the invariant points.

Invariant points will occur when the y-coordinate of any ordered pair on the graph of $f(x) = 2x + 2$ is equal to 1 or -1.

If $y = 1$:
$$1 = 2x + 2$$
$$-1 = 2x$$
$$-\frac{1}{2} = x$$
$$-0.5 = x$$

If $y = -1$:
$$-1 = 2x + 2$$
$$-3 = 2x$$
$$-\frac{3}{2} = x$$
$$-1.5 = x$$

Therefore, $(-0.5, 1)$ and $(-1.5, -1)$ are invariant points. Plot these points as shown.

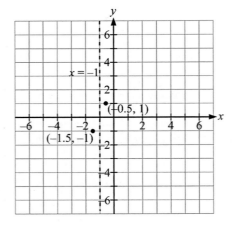

Step 3
Determine the y-intercept of the graph of $y = \frac{1}{2x + 2}$.

For $y = f(x) = 2x + 2$, solve for y when $x = 0$.
$$y = 2x + 2$$
$$y = 2(0) + 2$$
$$y = 2$$

The y-intercept of the graph of $f(x) = 2x + 2$ is $(0, 2)$.

Therefore, the y-intercept of the graph of $y = \frac{1}{2x + 2}$ is $\left(0, \frac{1}{2}\right)$ or $(0, 0.5)$.

ANSWERS AND SOLUTIONS

Step 4
From the invariant point (−0.5, 1), show the graph
of $y = \dfrac{1}{2x+2}$ increasing as x approaches the
vertical asymptote $x = -1$ from the right.

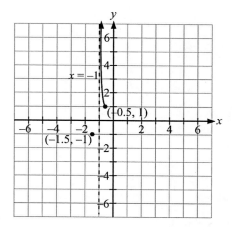

Step 5
From the invariant point (−1.5, −1), show the graph
of $y = \dfrac{1}{2x+2}$ decreasing as x approaches the
vertical asymptote $x = -1$ from the left.

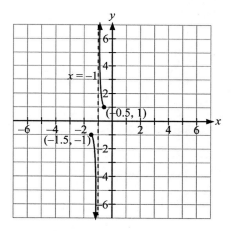

Step 6
From the invariant point (−1.5, −1) on the left,
show the graph of $y = \dfrac{1}{2x+2}$ approaching the
horizontal asymptote $y = 0$ from below the x-axis.
From the invariant point (0.5, 1) on the right, show
the graph of $y = \dfrac{1}{2x+2}$ approaching the horizontal
asymptote $y = 0$ from above the x-axis and
passing through the y-intercept (0, 0.5).

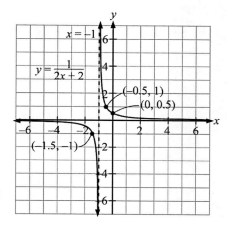

2. Step 1
Determine the vertical asymptotes of the function
$y = \dfrac{1}{x^2 - 9}$.

The x-intercepts of the graph of $f(x) = x^2 - 9$ are
(−3, 0) and (3, 0). Therefore, the graph of
$y = \dfrac{1}{x^2 - 9}$ will have vertical asymptotes at $x = -3$
and $x = 3$. Sketch the asymptotes as dotted lines.

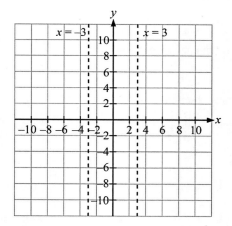

Step 2
Find the invariant points.

The invariant points will occur when the y-
coordinate of any ordered pair on the graph of
$f(x) = x^2 - 9$ is equal to 1 or −1.

If $y = 1$:
$$1 = x^2 - 9$$
$$10 = x^2$$
$$\pm\sqrt{10} = x$$

If $y = -1$:
$$-1 = x^2 - 9$$
$$8 = x^2$$
$$\pm\sqrt{8} = x$$
$$\pm 2\sqrt{2} = x$$

The invariant points are $\left(-\sqrt{10}, 1\right)$, $\left(\sqrt{10}, 1\right)$, $\left(-2\sqrt{2}, -1\right)$, and $\left(2\sqrt{2}, -1\right)$. Plot the points as shown.

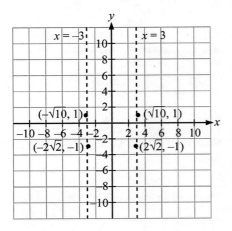

Step 3

Determine the y-intercept of $y = \dfrac{1}{x^2 - 9}$.

For $y = f(x) = x^2 - 9$, solve for y when $x = 0$.

$y = x^2 - 9$
$y = (0)^2 - 9$
$y = -9$

The y-intercept of the graph of $f(x) = x^2 - 9$ is $(0, -9)$.

Therefore, the y-intercept of the graph of $y = \dfrac{1}{x^2 - 9}$ is $\left(0, -\dfrac{1}{9}\right)$.

Step 4

From the invariant point $\left(-\sqrt{10}, 1\right)$, show the graph of $y = \dfrac{1}{x^2 - 9}$ increasing as x approaches the vertical asymptote $x = -3$ from the left.

From the invariant point $\left(\sqrt{10}, 1\right)$, show the graph of $y = \dfrac{1}{x^2 - 9}$ increasing as x approaches the vertical asymptote $x = 3$ from the right.

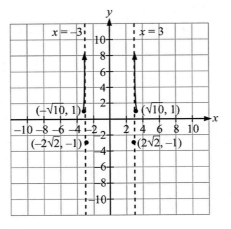

Step 5

From the invariant point $\left(-2\sqrt{2}, -1\right)$, show the graph of $y = \dfrac{1}{x^2 - 9}$ decreasing as x approaches the vertical asymptote $x = -3$ from the right.

From the invariant point $\left(2\sqrt{2}, -1\right)$, show the graph of $y = \dfrac{1}{x^2 - 9}$ decreasing as x approaches the vertical asymptote $x = 3$ from the left.

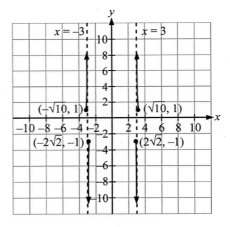

Step 6

From the invariant point $\left(-\sqrt{10}, 1\right)$ on the left and the invariant point $\left(\sqrt{10}, 1\right)$ on the right, show the graph of $y = \dfrac{1}{x^2 - 9}$ approaching the horizontal asymptote $y = 0$ from above the x-axis.

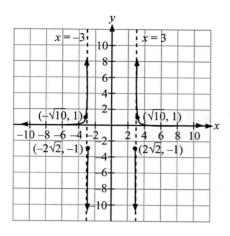

Step 7

From the invariant points $\left(-2\sqrt{2},-1\right)$ and $\left(2\sqrt{2},-1\right)$, show the graph of $y=\dfrac{1}{x^2-9}$ increasing to the y-intercept $\left(0,-\dfrac{1}{9}\right)$.

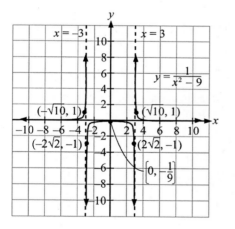

1. The horizontal asymptote of the function is at $y=0$.

    Determine the vertical asymptotes.

    Set the denominator equal to zero, and solve for x.
    $$0=4x^2-4x-48$$
    $$0=4(x^2-x-12)$$
    $$0=x^2-x-12$$
    $$0=x^2-4x+3x-12$$
    $$0=x(x-4)+3(x-4)$$
    $$0=(x-4)(x+3)$$
    $$x-4=0 \qquad x+3=0$$
    $$x=4 \qquad\ \ x=-3$$

    The vertical asymptotes are at $x=4$ and $x=-3$.

2. A function in the form $y=\dfrac{1}{f(x)}$ has a vertical asymptote when $f(x)=0$.

    Since the vertical asymptote is at $x=6$, then $f(6)=0$.

    Substitute 6 for x into the equation $ax-5=0$, and solve for a.
    $$ax+b=0$$
    $$a(6)-5=0$$
    $$6a=5$$
    $$a=\frac{5}{6}$$
    $$a \doteq 0.833\ 333$$

    To the nearest hundredth, the value of a is 0.83.

3. The points where the graphs of $y=f(x)$ and $y=\dfrac{1}{f(x)}$ intersect are called invariant points, and they occur when the y-coordinate of any ordered pair on the graph of $y=f(x)$ is either 1 or -1. The corresponding x-coordinate can be determined by substituting 1 or -1 for y in the equation $y=f(x)$ and then solving for x.

ANSWERS AND SOLUTIONS

ANSWERS AND SOLUTIONS

Step 1
Substitute 1 for y in the equation $y = f(x) = x + 3$, and solve for x.
$$1 = x + 3$$
$$-2 = x$$

The graphs intersect at $(-2, 1)$.

Step 2
Substitute -1 for y in the equation $y = f(x) = x + 3$, and solve for x.
$$-1 = x + 3$$
$$-4 = x$$

The graphs also intersect at $(-4, -1)$.

Thus, the graphs of $y = f(x)$ and $y = \dfrac{1}{f(x)}$ intersect at $(-2, 1)$ and $(-4, -1)$.

4. **B**
An invariant point for the graphs of $y = f(x)$ and $y = \dfrac{1}{f(x)}$ will occur when the y-coordinate of any ordered pair on the graph of $f(x) = x^2 - 3x - 17$ is equal to 1, since $y > 0$.

Determine the value of the x-coordinate that will give a y-coordinate of 1.

Let the equation of the function equal 1, and solve for x.
$$x^2 - 3x - 17 = 1$$
$$x^2 - 3x - 18 = 0$$
$$(x - 6)(x + 3) = 0$$
$$x = 6, -3$$

The points are $(6, 1)$ and $(-3, 1)$.

5. **Step 1**
Determine the vertical asymptote.

Set the denominator equal to zero, and solve for x.
$$3x - 48 = 0$$
$$3x = 48$$
$$x = 16$$

There is a vertical asymptote at $x = 16$.

Step 2
Determine the behaviour of the graph on the left of $x = 16$.

Calculate values of y as x approaches 16 from the left.

If $x = 15.99$:
$$y = \frac{1}{3x - 48}$$
$$y = \frac{1}{3(15.99) - 48}$$
$$y = \frac{1}{-0.03}$$
$$y = -33.\overline{33}$$

If $x = 15.9999$:
$$y = \frac{1}{3x - 48}$$
$$y = \frac{1}{3(15.9999) - 48}$$
$$y = \frac{1}{-0.0003}$$
$$y = -3\,333.\overline{33}$$

The y-values get smaller and smaller toward negative infinity.

Step 3
Determine the behaviour of the graph on the right of $x = 16$.

Calculate values of y as x approaches 16 from the right.

If $x = 16.01$:
$$y = \frac{1}{3x - 48}$$
$$y = \frac{1}{3(16.01) - 48}$$
$$y = \frac{1}{0.03}$$
$$y = 33.\overline{33}$$

If $x = 16.0001$:
$$y = \frac{1}{3x - 48}$$
$$y = \frac{1}{3(16.0001) - 48}$$
$$y = \frac{1}{0.0003}$$
$$y = 3\,333.\overline{33}$$

The y-values get larger and larger toward positive infinity.

Step 4
Determine the behaviour of the graph as $x \to -\infty$.

If $x = -20$:
$$y = \frac{1}{3x - 48}$$
$$y = \frac{1}{3(-20) - 48}$$
$$y = \frac{1}{-108}$$

If $x = -200$:
$$y = \frac{1}{3x - 48}$$
$$y = \frac{1}{3(-200) - 48}$$
$$y = \frac{1}{-648}$$

The y-values approach zero, but remain negative. The x-axis becomes a horizontal asymptote as $x \to -\infty$.

Step 5
Determine the behaviour of the graph as $x \to \infty$.

If $x = 20$:
$$y = \frac{1}{3x - 48}$$
$$y = \frac{1}{3(20) - 48}$$
$$y = \frac{1}{12}$$

If $x = 200$:
$$y = \frac{1}{3x - 48}$$
$$y = \frac{1}{3(200) - 48}$$
$$y = \frac{1}{552}$$

CASTLE ROCK RESEARCH · 194 · Copyright Protected

The y-values approach zero, but remain positive. The x-axis becomes the horizontal asymptote as $x \to \infty$.

6. Asymptotes on the graph of $y = \dfrac{1}{f(x)}$ occur

when $f(x) = 0$; these are the x-intercepts of the graph of $y = f(x)$.

The x-intercepts of the graph of $y = f(x)$ are $(-3, 0)$ and $(1, 0)$. Therefore, the graph of

$y = \dfrac{1}{f(x)}$ will have vertical asymptotes at $x = -3$

and $x = 1$.

7. **Step 1**
Determine the vertical asymptotes of the function

$y = \dfrac{1}{x - 7}$.

Solve for x when $x - 7 = 0$.
$x - 7 = 0$
$\quad x = 7$

Therefore, the vertical asymptote is at $x = 7$.

Sketch the asymptote as a dotted line.

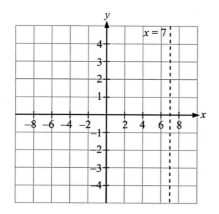

Step 2
Find the invariant points.

The invariant points will occur when the y-coordinate of any ordered pair on the graph of $f(x) = x - 7$ is equal to 1 or -1.

If $y = 1$:   If $y = -1$:
$1 = x - 7$ $-1 = x - 7$
$8 = x$ $6 = x$

The invariant points are $(8, 1)$ and $(6, -1)$.

Plot the points as shown.

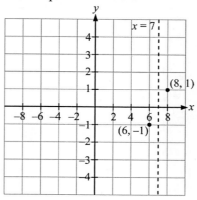

Step 3
Determine the y-intercept of the graph

of $y = \dfrac{1}{x - 7}$.

For $y = f(x) = x - 7$, solve for y when $x = 0$.
$y = x - 7$
$y = (0) - 7$
$y = -7$

The y-intercept of the graph of $f(x) = x - 7$ is $(0, -7)$. Therefore, the y-intercept of the graph of

$y = \dfrac{1}{x - 7}$ is $\left(0, -\dfrac{1}{7}\right)$.

Step 4
From the invariant point $(8, 1)$, show the graph of

$y = \dfrac{1}{x - 7}$ increasing as x approaches the vertical

asymptote $x = 7$ from the right.

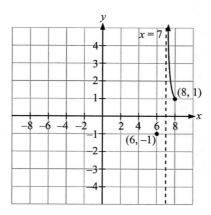

Step 5

From the invariant point $(6, -1)$, show the graph of

$y = \dfrac{1}{x-7}$ decreasing as x approaches the vertical

asymptote $x = 7$ from the left.

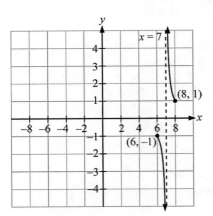

Step 6

From the invariant point $(6, -1)$ on the left, show

the graph of $y = \dfrac{1}{x-7}$ approaching the horizontal

asymptote $y = 0$ from below the x-axis and

passing through the y-intercept $\left(0, -\dfrac{1}{7}\right)$.

From the invariant point $(8, 1)$ on the right, show

the graph of $y = \dfrac{1}{x-7}$ approaching the horizontal

asymptote $y = 0$ from above the x-axis.

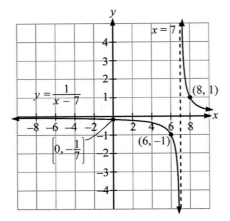

Credits

Every effort has been made to provide proper acknowledgement of the original source and to comply with copyright law. However, some attempts to establish original copyright ownership may have been unsuccessful. If copyright ownership can be identified, please notify Castle Rock Research Corp so that appropriate corrective action can be taken.

Some images in this document are from www.clipart.com, copyright (c) 2011 Jupiterimages Corporation.

NOTES

NOTES

199

NOTES

200

NOTES

NOTES

NOTES

BOOK ORDERING INFORMATION

SENIOR HIGH SCHOOL TITLES

Castle Rock Research offers the following resources to support Alberta students. You can order any of these materials online at:

www.castlerockresearch.com/store

SOLARO.com - Study Online		The KEY		SNAP	Prob Solved	Class Notes
$29.95 ea.*		**$29.95 ea.***		**$29.95 ea.***	**$19.95 ea.***	**$19.95 ea.***
Biology 30	Mathematics 30-1	Biology 30	Mathematics 30-1	Biology 20	Biology 20	Biology 20
Biology 20	Mathematics 30-2	Biology 20	Mathematics 30-2	Chemistry 30	Chemistry 30	Chemistry 30
Chemistry 30	Mathematics 30-3	Chemistry 30	Mathematics 20-1	Chemistry 20	Chemistry 20	Chemistry 20
Chemistry 20	Mathematics 20-1	Chemistry 20	Mathematics 10 C	Mathematics 30-1	Mathematics 30-1	Mathematics 30-1
Physics 30	Mathematics 20-2	English 30-1	Social Studies 30-1	Mathematics 30-2	Mathematics 30-2	Mathematics 30-2
Physics 20	Mathematics 20-3	English 30-2	Social Studies 30-2	Mathematics 31	Mathematics 31	Mathematics 31
Science 30	Mathematics 20-4	English 20-1	Social Studies 20-1	Mathematics 20-1	Mathematics 20-1	Mathematics 20-1
Science 20	Mathematics 10 C	English 10-1	Social Studies 10-1	Mathematics 10 C	Mathematics 10 C	Mathematics 10 C
Science 10	Mathematics 10-3	Physics 30		Physics 30	Physics 30	Physics 30
English 30-1	Mathematics 10-4	Physics 20		Physics 20	Physics 20	Physics 20
English 30-2	Social Studies 30-1	Science 10		Science 10	Science 10	Science 10
English 20-1	Social Studies 30-2					
English 20-2	Social Studies 20-1					
English 10-1	Social Studies 10-1					
English 10-2						

Prices do not include taxes or shipping.

Study online using **SOLARO,** with access to multiple courses available by either a monthly or an annual subscription.

The KEY Study Guide is specifically designed to assist students in preparing for unit tests, final exams, and provincial examinations.

The **Student Notes and Problems (SNAP) Workbook** contains complete explanations of curriculum concepts, examples, and exercise questions.

The **Problem Solved** contains exercise questions and complete solutions.

The **Class Notes** contains complete explanations of curriculum concepts.

If you would like to order Castle Rock resources for your school, please visit our school ordering page:

www.castlerockresearch.com/school-orders/